LIFE

Its Nature, Origin
and Development

ACADEMIC PAPERBACKS*

EDITED BY Henry Booker, D. Allan Bromley, Nicholas DeClaris,
W. Magnus, Alvin Nason, and A. Shenitzer

BIOLOGY

Design and Function at the Threshold of Life: The Viruses
HEINZ FRAENKEL-CONRAT
The Evolution of Genetics ARNOLD W. RAVIN
Isotopes in Biology GEORGE WOLF
Life: Its Nature, Origin, and Development A. I. OPARIN
Time, Cells, and Aging BERNARD L. STREHLER

ENGINEERING

A Vector Approach to Oscillations HENRY BOOKER
Dynamic Programming and Modern Control Theory RICHARD
BELLMAN and ROBERT KALABA

MATHEMATICS

Finite Permutation Groups HELMUT WIELANDT
Complex Numbers in Geometry I. M. YAGLOM
Elements of Abstract Harmonic Analysis GEORGE BACHMAN
Hamilton's Principle and Physical Systems B. R. GOSSICK
Geometric Transformations (in two volumes) P. S. MODENOV
and A. S. PARKHOMENKO
Introduction to p-Adic Numbers and Valuation Theory
GEORGE BACHMAN
Linear Operators in Hilbert Space WERNER SCHMEIDLER
The Method of Averaging Functional Corrections: Theory and
Applications A. Yu. LUCHKA
Noneuclidean Geometry HERBERT MESCHKOWSKI
Quadratic Forms and Matrices N. V. YEFIMOV
Representation Theory of Finite Groups MARTIN BURROW

PHYSICS

Crystals: Their Role in Nature and in Science CHARLES BUNN
Elementary Dynamics of Particles H. W. HARKNESS
Elementary Plane Rigid Dynamics H. W. HARKNESS
Mössbauer Effect: Principles and Applications
GUNTHER K. WERTHEIM
Potential Barriers in Semiconductors B. R. GOSSICK
Principles of Vector Analysis JERRY B. MARION

*Most of these volumes are also available in a cloth bound edition.

LIFE

Its Nature, Origin
and Development

A. I. OPARIN

Active member of the Academy of Sciences
of the U.S.S.R.

Translated from the Russian

by

ANN SYNGE

ACADEMIC PRESS
New York and London

This new Academic Press paperback edition, first published in 1964, is an unabridged and unaltered republication of the first edition published in 1962 by Oliver and Boyd Ltd. Tweeddale Court, 14 High Street, Edinburgh 1, Scotland. It is published by special arrangement with Oliver and Boyd Ltd.

Edition for all the Americas, except Canada published by

ACADEMIC PRESS INC.
111 Fifth Avenue
New York, New York, 10003

All Rights Reserved

This book may not be reproduced by any means, in whole or part, without the written permission of the Publishers

TRANSLATION © ANN SYNGE

First Printing, 1964
Second Printing, 1966

PRINTED IN THE UNITED STATES OF AMERICA

PREFACE

THIS book is a natural extension of the work in the field of the problem of the origin of life which I have been carrying on for many years. Until quite recently this problem and the problem of the essential nature of life were regarded as two independent problems. The first was almost entirely ignored by scientific research workers, while the concept of the essential nature of life was treated purely metaphysically, completely divorced from its origin.

Nowadays scientists are coming to realise more and more that these two problems are really one, that the nature of life and its origin and development can only be studied in the light of their indissoluble association.

This book is an attempt to approach the problem of the essential nature of life from such an angle.

I wish to express my deep gratitude to Candidate N. S. Gel'man for the help she has given me in my work on this book.

A. OPARIN

TRANSLATOR'S NOTE

The bibliography at the end of this book gives references to some of the works mentioned in the text. More detailed bibliographies covering the whole subject may be found in the works listed there under the name of Professor Oparin. They are works of reference and, therefore, are fully indexed. This is an introductory work and, as it has a very detailed contents list, I did not feel there was any need to compile an index.

A. S.

CONTENTS

CHAPTER I

THE NATURE OF LIFE

CHAPTER II

THE ORIGIN OF LIFE

CHAPTER III

THE EARLIEST PERIOD OF THE DEVELOPMENT OF LIFE

CHAPTER IV

THE FURTHER EVOLUTION OF LIFE

CHAPTER V

CONCLUSION

Figures 2 — 6, 8, 9, 12, 15, 16, and 17 are grouped together following page 52.

THE NATURE OF LIFE

THE EXTENT OF LIFE

Lᴵꜰᴇ—the word is so easy to understand yet so enigmatic for any thoughtful person. One would have thought that the meaning of this word would have been clear and the same for all ages and all peoples. Nevertheless, we know that, during the many centuries of human cultural history, there have been irreconcilable conflicts as to how it should properly be understood.

Even the question of what is alive, which of the objects in the world around us are imbued or endowed with life, the extent of the realm of life or its scope, have been defined and are still defined in various totally different ways. We have, as it were, a whole multicoloured spectrum of different opinions. At the one end of this spectrum we find the views of those philosophers and scientists who believe that life is a general property, inalienable from all matter, and who therefore extend the realm of life to cover all objects in the universe.

On the other hand, the philosophers of the opposite end of the spectrum arbitrarily restrict the scope of life to the compass of human existence, or may even maintain that life is the prerogative of one single thinking subject.

The first of these opinions owes its origin to the ancient Greek hylozoists. According to Aristotle, even Thales the founder of the Miletian school of philosophy (who was alive about 600 B.C.) considered magnets to be animate on account of their ability to attract iron. More than 2000 years later, in the 17th century, the Dutch philosopher and materialist, Spinoza, maintained that stones think and that all natural bodies are animate, while even 100 years later still (also in Holland), the French philosopher Robinet published a book called *On Nature* in which he acknowledged that all matter was living and even considered the stars in heaven as living organic bodies.

Even in our own times, many engineers and physicists are ready to consider the most complicated modern mechanisms and automata as being alive, just as Descartes compared organisms to water clocks or mills, or La Mettrie referred to man as an extremely well-educated machine. Some present-day chemists and geneticists follow Diderot in an attempt to assign life even to individual molecules of organic substances.

On the other hand, it is understood by anyone that, if some writer or philosopher speaks, in one of his works, about the significance or value of life, or about its aim, then he is referring only to human life, to that " striving towards good " which, according to Tolstoï, constitutes the main aspiration of life and is understood as such by all men.

This last expression of opinion is taken from Tolstoï's treatise *On Life*. In it Tolstoï censures the experimental scientists or, as he calls them, the scribes* for using the actual word ' life ', in that by cunning sophistry they have invented a conventional scientific Volapük in which words do not correspond with what all ordinary laymen understand by them. Tolstoï justifiably recommends that " a man is bound, by every word, to mean that which all indisputably understand alike ".

It seems to me that if we follow this wise advice we shall be able to find a way out of the present confusing labyrinth of contradictory opinions on the question of the delimitation of the realm of life, although the way out which we shall find will be far from the same as that of which Tolstoï approved. Any ordinary person looking at the world around him will infallibly sort it into the kingdom of the lifeless or inorganic, and that of living things. In all places and at all times he will see that life is not simply scattered about all over the place, but only exists in individual organisms which are separate from their environment; so that the sum of these organisms constitutes the realm of life, the world of living things. This world exhibits a colossal variety, including plants, animals and microbes, which are very diverse and which, at first glance, would hardly seem to have anything in common. Nevertheless, anybody, even without any scientific experience, can

* L. Tolstoï is here using the term ' scribe ' in the bad sense in which it is used in the gospels " scribes and Pharisees."

easily observe what they do have in common and what enables one to include in the one category of ' living being ' a man and a tree, a whale and a tiny beetle or blade of grass, a bird and a shapeless mollusc.

When the simple glass polisher from Amsterdam, Leeuwenhoek, first saw microbes of various kinds through his magnifying glass, he unhesitatingly designated them as living things (*viva animalcula*), although some of them, such as the cocci, which Leeuwenhoek drew with his own hand, could not move and had none of the other external features of living things.

On perceiving that living things have something in common, which relates them to one another, one distinguishes them from the objects of the inorganic world which lack that ' something ' i.e. which lack life. Thus, even by his unaided observation of the world around him, any ordinary person can establish the most elementary, but also the most general definition of the extent of life or the area embraced by its natural realm. Life is a property of any organism, from the highest to the lowest, but it does not exist in inorganic natural objects, no matter how complicated their structure may be. It is very possible that, in the unbounded extent of the universe, there exists a multitude of extremely complicated and highly-evolved forms of movement and organisation of matter, of which we, as yet, have no suspicion, but it would be quite unjustifiable to call any of these forms ' life ' if they differed in essential principles from that life which is represented on our planet by a whole multitude of organisms of different forms. It would be better to think up a special new word to denote these forms of organisation when it is required.

We have thus marked out the region of nature, the category of objects which are pertinent to our enquiries about life. This means that, in what follows, we can avoid many of the mistakes which are rather common in scientific literature, by keeping strictly to the terms of reference laid down above. Of course, what has been given is not, by any means, a definition of life. To give that one would have to solve the problem of the nature of that ' something ' which is characteristic only of the world of living things and which is absent from the objects of inorganic nature.

THE CONFLICT BETWEEN IDEALISM AND MATERIALISM
AS TO THE ESSENTIAL NATURE OF LIFE

From the earliest times, even until the present day, this problem of the essential nature of life has always been a battle-field in the embittered war which has been waged between the two irreconcilable philosophic camps of idealism and materialism.

The representatives of the idealist camp see, as the essence of life, some sort of eternal supramaterial origin which is inaccessible to experiment. This is the 'psyche' of Plato, the 'entelechy' of Aristotle, the 'immortal soul' or 'particle of divinity' of various religious doctrines and faiths, Kant's 'inneres Prinzip der Kausalität', the 'Weltgeist' of the Hegelians, the 'life force' of the vitalists and the 'dominant' of the neovitalists, and other such concepts.

From this point of view, matter, in the sense of that objective reality which we observe directly and study experimentally, is in itself and as such, lifeless and inert. It serves only as the material from which the spirit or soul creates a living being, gives it form, adapts its structure to functional needs, endows it with the power of breathing and moving and, in general, makes it alive. And when the soul leaves the organism and death takes place, there remains but the lifeless material envelope, a rotten, decomposing corpse.

This concept of death as the departure from the body of the soul, which constitutes the essence of life, is, in fact, the basis of a definition of life which is widely held and even appears in a number of encyclopaedias, namely, that life is the contrary of death. This, however, pushes out of sight the fact that the living can only properly be contrasted with the lifeless, not with the dead. It is obvious that the dead body is a product of life for, in the absence of life, that is in an inorganic world, a corpse could never occur on its own.

Even if one starts from idealistic premises one can, of course, make an objective study of particular organisms and their organs, but it is inherently impossible to reach an under-standing of the essence of life itself by experimental, materialistic means, as this essence is of a supramaterial or spiritual nature. Only by means of speculative introspection can one approach an understanding of that divine principle which we bear within ourselves. We can only passively contemplate all the rest of the world of living things and marvel at the wisdom of the Creator Who made them. And naturally there can be no question of man making any change or transformation in living nature if one adopts this position.

Materialists approach the problem of the essence of life from a diametrically opposite viewpoint. Basing their arguments on the facts obtained by science they assert that life, like all the rest of the world, is material and does not require for its understanding the acceptance of a spiritual origin which is not amenable to experimental study. On the contrary, objective study of the world around us is, for the materialist, not only a hopeful way of leading us to an understanding of the very essence of life, but it also enables us to alter living nature purposefully in a way favourable to mankind.

Wide circles of biological scientists, either consciously or intuitively, base their investigations on a materialistic concept of living nature and, in following this line, they are always enriching the science of life by their work and bringing us closer to an understanding of the essence of life.

MECHANICAL AND DIALECTICAL CONCEPTS OF LIFE

However, even within the limits of the materialistic concept of life, its essence may be interpreted in various ways.

According to the mechanistic view, which prevailed in the scientific world of last century, and which is partly retained even now, the understanding of life in general comprises simply a complete explanation in terms of physics and chemistry, a complete account of all living phenomena as physical and chemical processes. If one adopts this position there is no place for any specifically biological laws of nature. In reality there is only one law which governs both the inorganic world and all the phenomena occurring in living organisms. This is, in fact, to deny that there is any qualitative difference between organisms and inorganic objects. We thus reach a position where we must say either that inorganic objects are alive or that life does not really exist. Thus, by a logical development of the mechanistic outlook which has been explained, we are forced to a conclusion which is fundamentally opposed to the view which we adopted earlier. However, in contradistinction to this, one must be quite clear that acceptance of the material nature of life does not mean that one must deny that it has specific characteristics and that living things show qualitative differences from inorganic objects. One must not do as the mechanists and regard everything which is not included in physics and chemistry as being vitalistic or supernatural. On the contrary, the forms of organisation and motion of matter may be very varied. To deny this variety is to indulge in oversimplification.

According to the dialectical materialist view, matter is in constant motion and proceeds through a series of stages of development. In the course of this progress there arise ever newer, more complicated and more highly evolved forms of motion of matter having new properties which were not previously present. There can be no doubt that, for a long period after the formation of our planet, there was no life on it. Obviously, all the things which existed on it at that time simply obeyed the laws of physics and chemistry. However, in the process of development of matter on the Earth, the first and most primitive organisms arose, that is to say, life came into being as a qualitatively new form of motion. When this happened, the old laws of physics and chemistry naturally continued to operate, but now they were supplemented by new and more complicated biological laws which had not operated before.

Thus, life is material in nature but its properties are not limited to those of matter in general. Only living beings possess it. This is a special form of the movement of matter, qualitatively different from that of the inorganic world, and the organism has specific biological properties and ways of behaving and does not merely follow the rules governing inorganic nature. Therefore a dialectical materialist will even formulate the problem of understanding life in a different way from a mechanist. For the latter it consists in a more complete explanation of life in terms of physics and chemistry. For the dialectical materialist, on the other hand, the important thing about understanding life is the establishment of its qualitative difference from other forms of matter, i.e. that difference which obliges us to regard life as a special form of the motion of matter.

ATTEMPTS TO FORMULATE DEFINITIONS OF LIFE

This difference has found, and still finds, a greater or less reflection in the definitions of life formulated and expounded by the scientists and thinkers of last century and those of our own time. It is just in their setting out of this difference between the living and the non-living that one can perceive the objective and essential value of these definitions in spite of their absolute contradictoriness and their astounding variety.

At the beginning of his remarkable book, *Leçons sur les phénomènes de la vie communs aux animaux et aux végétaux* (1878-1879), Claude Bernard produces a large number of definitions of life which had been made before that time, but he does so simply in order to show that, in general, any *a priori* definition of life is always chimerical and scientifically unprofitable. However, he also believes that life can be understood completely if approached *a posteriori*, by establishing the characteristic features which differentiate living creatures from non-living bodies. This is certainly not easy and, in doing it we are beset with considerable difficulties and doubts, but all the time we are getting closer to solving our problem.

In an American encyclopaedia of 1944 it is stated that there is no single satisfactory definition of life, for, while some include too many phenomena, others suffer from too narrow limitations.

We believe that this is because, in most cases, people try to characterise life as a single point while it is, in fact, a long line, comprising the whole of that section of the development of matter lying between the origin of life on the Earth and our own time, and including among its manifestations the most primitive organisms as well as more highly developed plants and animals, especially man. With the appearance of man, however, there arises a new social form of motion of matter which is more complicated and highly evolved than life and which is characterised by its own peculiar features and by the special laws of development of human society.

It is therefore completely wrong to try to characterise the 'line of life' simply on the basis of one point, whether that point lies at the beginning, the middle or the end. In fact, if we try to define life in terms of the characteristics which arose at the very beginning of its emergence on the Earth, we have to exclude from among its features, not merely consciousness, but also respiration, which obviously did not take place among the earliest organisms. On the other hand, if we define life on the basis of phenomena which are typical only of the more highly developed living things, we shall risk relegating the anaerobic bacteria, as well as many primitive organisms, to the category of non-living bodies belonging to inorganic nature.

When Engels made his remarkable definition of life as the " mode of existence of albuminous bodies " he immediately made reservations, indicating the incompleteness of the definition. " Our definition of life ", he wrote, " is naturally very inadequate, inasmuch as, far from including *all* the phenomena of life, it has to be limited to those which are the most common and the simplest. From a scientific standpoint all definitions are of little value. In order to gain a really exhaustive knowledge of what life is, we should have to go through all the forms in which it appears, from the lowest up to the highest ".

Thus for an exhaustive understanding of life it is necessary to have an understanding of the whole gamut of its characteristic features, starting with those extremely elementary ones, with which the first living beings were endowed, and finishing with the most complicated manifestations of higher nervous activity in animals and man, in which the biological stage of the development of matter culminates. Among this multitude of features characteristic of life, manifested at the very outset of its development and becoming more complicated in the course of its further evolution and increasing complexity, special mention must be made of that clearly defined, specific inter-action between the organism and its environment which runs, like a red thread, along the 'line of life' and is a characteristic of all living things, the lowest as well as the highest, but which is absent from the objects of the inorganic world.

THE SPECIFIC INTERACTION BETWEEN THE ORGANISM
AND ITS ENVIRONMENT

An organism can live and maintain itself only so long as it is continually exchanging material and energy with its environment. As food, drink and gaseous material, various substances of a chemical nature foreign to the organism enter into it. In the organism they undergo far-reaching changes and transformations as a result of which they are converted into the material of the organism itself. That is to say, they are turned into chemical compounds which are, in some degree, similar to those of which the living body is already composed. This is the ascending limb of biological metabolism known as assimilation. In the course of the interaction of substances from outside with the material of the organism, however, the opposite process also occurs continually and is known as dissimilation. The substances of the living body do not remain unchanged. They are broken down fairly quickly to liberate the energy latent in them and the products of their breakdown are discharged into the surrounding medium.

Our bodies flow like rivulets, their material is renewed like water in a stream. This was what the ancient Greek dialectician Heraclitus taught. Certainly the flow, or simply the stream of water emerging from a tap, enables us to understand in their simplest form many of the essential features of such flowing, or open systems as are represented by the particular case of the living body. If the tap is not far open and the pressure in the water cistern remains constant, the external form of the water flowing from the tap remains almost unchanged, as though it were congealed. We know, however, that this form is merely the visible expression of a continual flow of particles of water, which are constantly passing through the stream at a steady rate and emerging from it. If we disturb the relationship between the rates of input and output or the steady process of movement of its particles, the stream, as such, disappears, for the very existence of the stream depends on the steady passage of ever-renewed water molecules through it.

On this analogy the constancy of the external form, and even of the most detailed internal structure of the living being, is merely the visible expression of the constancy of the sequence of processes going on within it as a result of the extremely intricate balancing of the two contrary phenomena already noted, i.e. assimilation and dissimilation. The prolonged existence of a living system in which breakdown and decay are going on all the time is entirely due to this balance. In the place of each molecule or structure which breaks down a new and analogous one appears as a freshly synthesised formation. Thus the organism maintains its form, structure and chemical composition unchanged while its material is continually changing.

Organisms are, thus, not static but stationary or flowing systems. Their ability to exist for a longer or shorter time under given environmental conditions does not depend on their being at rest or unchanging. On the contrary, it depends on the constancy of their movement, i.e. their metabolism.

From a purely chemical point of view, metabolism is merely the sum of a large number of comparatively simple reactions of oxidation, reduction, aldol condensation, hydrolysis, transamination, phosphorylation, cyclisation etc. Each of these reactions can be reproduced, even outside the organism, as there is nothing specifically connected with life about them.

The peculiarity which distinguishes life qualitatively from all other forms of motion of matter (and in particular from inorganic flowing systems) is that, in the living body, the many tens and hundreds of thousands of individual chemical reactions, which, in their sum, make up the metabolism, are not only strictly co-ordinated in time and space, not merely co-operating harmoniously in a single sequence of self-renewal, but the whole of this sequence is directed in an orderly way towards the continual self-preservation and self-reproduction of the living body as a whole. They are extremely well adapted to solving the problem of the existence of the organism under a given set of environmental conditions.

THE ' PURPOSIVENESS ' OF THE ORGANISATION
OF LIVING BODIES

This flowing character of the interaction of living bodies with the medium around them, and, what is most important, the amazingly efficient adaptation of the organisation of this interaction to the task of self-preservation and self-reproduction of the system under a given set of external conditions, all that which has been referred to by many authors as the ' adaptation of form to function ' or ' purposiveness ' in the structure of such a system, is so objectively obvious and makes such a forcible impression on the eyes of those who study living nature that, in one form or another, it figures in the majority of even the most varied definitions of life formulated during the course of many centuries and put forward by members of the most dissimilar schools of philosophy and scientific thought.

The presence in all organisms, without exception, of an adaptation of form to function was noted even by Aristotle who, in his writings, was the first to be able to generalise from the extensive accumulation of biological material which was available at that time. Aristotle designated this specific property of living things as the ' entelechy ' underlying life or the ' principle having its aim within itself '.

In one form or another Aristotle's teaching about ' entelechy ' has left its mark on all idealistic definitions of life. It is reflected in various religious creeds and philosophic teachings and has lasted through many centuries to reach our own 20th century in the works of Reinke, Driesch and other contemporary students of vitalism.

In their investigations of life, however, the representatives of the materialist camp naturally could not overlook this specific feature of it. Many of them, following Descartes, defined the vital phenomena of plants and animals merely as responsive reactions of a specifically constructed bodily mechanism to the external influence of the environment. Others saw the orderly direction of metabolism as the specific property which distinguished organisms from non-living things.

In this connection Claude Bernard wrote:

" L'édifice organique est le siége d'un perpétuel mouvement nutritif qui ne laisse de repos à aucune partie: chacune, sans cesse ni trère, s'alimente dans le milieu qui l'entoure et y rejette ses dechettes et ses produits. Cette renovation moleculaire est insaisissable pour le regard; mais, comme nous en voyons le debut et le fin, l'entrée et la sortie des substances, nous en concevons les phases intermediaires, et nous nous représentons un courant de matière qui traverse incessamment l'organisme et le renouvelle dans sa substance en le maintenant dans sa forme.

L'universalité d'un tel phénomène chez la plante et chez l'animal et dans toutes leurs parties, sa constance, qui ne souffre pas d'arrèt, en font un signe général de la vie, que quelques physiologistes ont employé à sa definition." *

" There is one expression which must be applied to all organisms ", wrote Engels, " and that is adaptation ". Later he puts forward his own definition of life: " Life is the mode of existence of albuminous substances and this mode of existence essentially consists in the constant self-renewal of the chemical constituents of these substances by nutrition and excretion ".

In our own times, Perret and later, Bernal, have tried to define life in the following terms which are, perhaps, rather complicated for non-specialists.

" Life is a potentially self-perpetuating open system of linked organic reactions, catalysed stepwise and almost isothermally by complex and specific organic catalysts which are themselves produced by the system ".

" The organism represents an entity as a system only in conjunction with the conditions necessary for its life " states a representative of the Michurinist school of biology.

Thus the universal ' purposiveness ' of the organisation of living beings is an objective and self-evident fact which cannot be ignored by any thoughtful student of nature. The rightness or wrongness of the definition of life advanced by us, and also of many others, depends on what interpretation one gives to

---

* " The organic structure is the seat of perpetual nutritional movement which leaves no part of it at rest: each part nourishes itself, without rest or pause, from the medium surrounding it and discharges its wastes and products into that same medium. This molecular renewal is not perceptible to the eye, but, as we see the beginning and the end of it, the entry and discharge of substances, we can imagine the intermediate stages and we picture to ourselves a flow of matter, incessantly passing through the organism and renewing its substance while maintaining its form.

The universality of such a phenomenon in plants and animals and in all parts of them, as well as their constancy, which never undergoes arrest, make it a general sign of life which some physiologists have used for its definition."

the word ' purposiveness ' and what one believes to be its essential nature and origin.

The idealists see this ' purposiveness ' as the fulfilment of some predetermined plan of a deity or ' universal intellect '. The materialists, on the other hand, use the expression (for lack of a better one) as the shortest way of characterising the direction of the organisation of the whole living system towards its self-preservation and self-reproduction under given environmental conditions, as well as to describe the suitability of the structure of the separate parts of the living system to the most efficient and harmonious performance of those vitally necessary functions which the particular part subserves.

The extremely highly developed adaptation of the structure of the individual organs to the performance of their functions and the general ' purposiveness ' of the whole organisation of life is seen to be extremely precise even on a very superficial acquaintance with higher living things. As we have already pointed out, it was noticed a long time ago and found expression in the Aristotelian ' entelechy '. It had been considered to be essentially mystical and supernatural until Darwin gave a rational, materialistic explanation of the way in which this ' purposiveness ' arose in higher organisms by means of natural selection.

' Purposiveness ' of structure does not, however, manifest itself solely in the more highly organised creatures, it pervades the whole living world from the top to the bottom, right down to the most elementary forms of life. It is necessary to every living body but in the absence of the living body there would be no ' purposiveness ' under natural conditions. It would therefore be fruitless for us to seek its explanation simply in terms of the laws of the inorganic world, i.e. the laws of physics and chemistry. The ' purposiveness ' which is characteristic of the organisation of all living things can only be understood if one understands the specific interaction between the organism and its environment in terms of the Darwinian principle of natural selection. This new biological law could only arise on the basis of the establishment of life and therefore lifeless, inorganic bodies lack ' purposiveness '. The striking exception to this rule is the machine.

ATTEMPTS TO TREAT THE ORGANISM AS A MACHINE

It is, of course, impossible to doubt that the principle on which any machine is constructed is that of adapting its structure or external organisation to the performance of the particular specific job which is its work. From this point of view the comparison between the machine and the organism forces itself upon one. In the course of m..ny centuries it has been widely used by many philosophers and scientists, in their attempts to solve the problem of the essential nature of life. The only thing that has changed in these attempts, in the course of the various periods of development of science, has been the opinion as to which of the points common to the organism and the machine ought to be taken into consideration, as being the features most characteristic of life. The way in which the problem was posed and the attempt to describe the organism as a machine of some sort or another has, however, remained essentially unchanged. Undoubtedly the ideas of each age tend to be expressed in terms of its technology. In his book,* N. Wiener very pertinently refers to the 17th century and the early part of the 18th century as " the age of clocks ", the end of the 18th century and the whole of the 19th century as " the age of steam-engines " and our own times as " the age of communication and control ".

In the age of clocks the world was represented by man as a huge mechanism which had been wound up once and for all time. People saw, as the basis of all existence, mechanical motion, the displacement of bodies in space, taking place according to Newton's laws of motion. Life was also discussed from this point of view, as being merely a special kind of mechanical motion. The spontaneous movement of animals and their organs through space may serve as the clearest expression of this. According to the ideas of that time, therefore, the organism is nothing but a " very complicated machine, the structure of which is, nevertheless, completely comprehensible. Its movement depends entirely on its structure and on the pressure and on the collision of particles of matter like

---

* *Cybernetics or control and communication in the animal and in the machine.* New York: Wiley (1949).

the wheels of a water clock " (Descartes). Anatomy therefore occupied the most important place in the study of life at that time.

However, in the next period of the development of science, the age of steam-engines, physiology began, to a greater and greater extent, to aspire to this place and the rôle of mechanics in the study of life was taken over by energetics.

The prototype of the living creature was now thought of, not as a watch, but as a heat engine. The analogy put forward by Lavoisier between respiration and the burning of fuel was a great step forward. Food is simply the fuel we throw into the furnace of our organism and its importance can therefore be assessed completely in terms of calories. The guiding principles of that time in connection with the understanding of life were those of the conservation and degradation of energy. The first law of thermodynamics, that of the conservation of energy, was found to be universally applicable, both to organisms and to mechanisms.

The second law was a more complicated matter. This is the law which expresses the statistical tendency of nature towards disorder, the tendency to even out energy and thus to devalue it in isolated systems, which is expressed in general terms as the increase of entropy in these systems. If one were to put such a system in uniform conditions and leave it alone, then all the phenomena occurring within it would very soon cease and the system as a whole would come to an end. It would thus attain the unchanging state in which nothing would happen. Physicists call this state 'thermodynamic equilibrium' or 'maximum entropy'.

In organisms, on the other hand, not only does entropy not increase, it may even decrease. Thus, one might say that the fundamental law of physics was a tendency towards disorder or an increase in entropy, while that of biology, on the contrary, was a tendency to increasing organisation or a decrease in entropy. Some idealist philosophers, such as A. Bergson, defined life as the " struggle against entropy " and even saw, in this contradiction between physics and biology, a reason for accepting the supernatural nature of life.

Now, however, we know that the contradiction is only apparent. Living things can never exist as isolated systems. On the contrary, as we have said above, it is characteristic of living organisms that they constantly interact with their environment and, by virtue of this fact, they must be regarded as 'flowing' or 'open' systems. The stationary (but not static) state in which they exist is maintained constant, not because they are in a state of 'maximum entropy', or because their free energy is at a minimum (as is the case in the thermodynamic equilibrium), but because the open system is continually receiving free energy from the medium around it in an amount which compensates for the decrease taking place within the system.

Wiener maintains that the ability to act against the general tendency to the increase of entropy is to be found, not only in organisms, but also in machines which have certain specific ways of interacting with the world outside them. In this way he thinks that machines can create a certain local zone of organisation around themselves.

CYBERNETICS

This concept ushers in the third and present period of the history of the problem, the age of communications and control which has superseded the age of steam-engines.

"There is, in electrical engineering", he writes, "a split which is known in Germany as a split between the technique of strong currents and the technique of weak currents, and which we (in the U.S.A. and Great Britain) know as the distinction between power and communication engineering. It is this split which separates the age which is just past from that in which we are now living". Communication engineering may make use of currents of any strength and may use enormous motors, but it differs from power engineering in that it is fundamentally interested in the exact reproduction of signals and not in the way in which energy is used.

The energy consumed by an electronic valve may be almost entirely wasted, but nevertheless the valve may be a very effective means of carrying out a necessary operation. Similarly, the efficiency of the work of our nervous systems cannot be calculated simply from the point of view of the rational utilisation of the comparatively small amount of energy which reaches the neurones from the blood stream.

Organisms are effectively coupled to the world around them, not merely by their overall metabolism and energy balance, but also by the flow of communications inwards and outwards, the flow of impressions received and actions performed. The extremely well organised and highly differentiated higher nervous activity of man and animals may serve as a particularly clear example of the relationship. Wiener, however, maintains that it is possible to produce a very far-reaching analogy between this activity and the work of contemporary self-regulating machines and automata. Photo-electric elements and other light receptors, radiolocating systems, apparatus for the registration of the potential of hydrogen ions, thermometers, manometers, all sorts of microphones etc. are the equivalents of the sensory organs and serve as mechanisms for receiving information. The effector organs of the machine may be electric motors, solenoids, heating elements and other similar devices. Between the receptor mechanisms and the effector organs of such machines as, for example, the contemporary quick-acting electronic calculating machine, there are intermediate groups of elements, a central regulating system which might be regarded as being analogous with the brain of animals or man.

The object of this system is to co-ordinate the incoming messages in such a way as to bring about the desired reaction by the executive organs. As well as the information reaching this central regulating machine from the outside world, it also receives information about the working of the executive organs themselves. This is what is known as ' feedback ' and it permits recording of the fulfilment or non-fulfilment of its own tasks by the machine itself. " Moreoever ", writes Wiener, " the information received by the automat need not necessarily be used at once but may be delayed or stored so as to become available at some future time. This is the analogue of memory. Finally, as long as the automaton is running, its very rules of operation are susceptible to some change on the basis of the data which have passed through its receptors, and this is not unlike the process of learning ".

Thus, in the transition from the age of the steam engine to the age of communication and control, the prototype of the living thing is becoming the electronic calculating machine, the study of nutrition gives place to the study of the physiology of the central nervous system and energetics is exchanged for cybernetics, which is the scientific study of the reception, transmission, storage, transformation and use of information by regulating apparatus, regardless of whether it is made ' of metal or of flesh ', i.e. whether it is a machine or an organism.

Like any new branch of knowledge, cybernetics is developing very quickly. In the very short period of its existence it has therefore succeeded in enriching with new ideas and achievements both science and, especially, contemporary technology, in its efforts at maximal automation in the direction of the productive processes. Furthermore, the latest developments in automats and in calculating machines have already advanced so far that the results of experiments planned or already carried out with them may, in many cases, be used in efforts to achieve a rational explanation of the phenomena which take place during the functioning of the nervous system and in many other processes. The understandable attractiveness of these successes as well as the extensive (though little-justified) use of neurophysiological, psychological and even sociological terminology in cybernetics, has now created a situation in which many contemporary authors are beginning to think that machines which can solve complicated mathematical problems, make translations from one language into another and, in general, carry out many tasks normally considered as brain work, must, in some way, be alive and, therefore, they have come to regard cybernetics as being a fundamentally new and universal road to the understanding of the very essence of life.

Of course, this is wrong. As we have pointed out earlier, attempts have been made, many years ago, to attribute life to machines. The only thing that has changed is the opinion as to what aspect one should concentrate on; movement, energetics, communication or some other property common to organisms and machines which is susceptible to explanation in terms of the laws of physics and chemistry. The basic stimulus which induces investigators to attribute life to machines is always the same. It is as follows. ' Purposiveness ' in the organisation of living things is what differentiates them in principle from the objects of the inorganic world. Apart from organisms, machines are the only things which show such 'purposiveness' in their structure. Furthermore, the work of machines can be completely known in terms of physics and chemistry. This identification of living things with machines was therefore viewed as the one and only way of saving science from the mystical entelechy of the vitalists, the bridge which will carry us over from physics and chemistry to biology.

Of course, we may, and should, try to understand the physical and chemical basis of the various vital phenomena by means of the construction and study of models which will reproduce the same phenomena as occur in organisms but in a simplified form. In doing so, however, we must always remember that we are dealing with models and not confuse them with living things. We must always take into account the differences as well as the similarities between the model and the real thing. Only thus can we avoid very dangerous oversimplification and those mistakes which have always cost mankind dear and which have only been corrected by science at the expense of a tremendous effort. However great the complexity or intricacy of its organisation, an electronic calculating machine is still further apart in its nature from a human being than is, for example, the simplest bacterium, although this has not got the differentiated nervous system which the machine imitates so successfully.

Unfortunately this difference is usually slurred over in cybernetic literature. It may be that this is, to some extent, justifiable when we wish to concentrate our attention solely on the general rules of communication and not on any particular systems. However, if the aim of our studies is the understanding of the nature of life, then it is, in principle, impermissible to ignore the difference between organisms and mechanisms.

APPRAISAL OF CONTEMPORARY MECHANISTIC HYPOTHESES

The first difference between machines and living things to strike the eye is the material of which the different systems are made and their actual nature.

Those who hold the theory that living things are machines usually tend to ignore this difference on the ground that the work of a machine depends, essentially, on its structure and not on the material of which it is made. In this connection Jost has written: " We may construct a machine of steel or of brass and this will certainly affect its durability and accuracy but not the nature of the work it does ". One might even construct a machine not of metal but of plastic or some other organic material and thus approximate its composition to the chemical composition of a living thing.

Such considerations are, however, radically unsound. The fact that living things are, in Engels' words, " albuminous bodies ", that they include in their composition proteins, nucleic acids, lipids, specific carbohydrates and other multifarious organic compounds is by no means to be regarded as an incidental circumstance of only slight significance. The composition of the living body is the very factor which determines its flowing character. In particular, it is only by understanding the highly specific features of the structure of proteins that we can understand the immediate causes underlying the determinate sequences of individual reactions in metabolism, that is to say, their co-ordination in time.

Any organic substance can react in very many different ways, it has tremendous chemical possibilities, but outside the living body it is extremely ' lazy ' or slow about exploiting these possibilities. Inside the living thing, however, organic substances undergo extremely rapid chemical transformation. This is due to the catalytic properties of proteins. If any organic substance is to play a real part in metabolism it must enter into chemical combination with some protein-enzyme, and form with it a particular, very active and unstable intermediate compound. If it does not do so its chemical potentialities will be realised so slowly that they will be insignificant in the quickly flowing process of life.

Owing to its extreme specificity, each enzyme will only form intermediate compounds with a particular substance (its substrate) and will only catalyse strictly determined individual reactions. The rates at which these reactions take place within the living body may therefore vary greatly, depending, in the first place, on the presence of a set of enzymes, and also on their catalytic activity. This latter can be greatly changed by internal physical and chemical circumstances and also by the action of the external medium. This sort of mobile relationship between the rates of individual biochemical reactions is, in fact, a prerequisite for the determinate sequences and concordances of these reactions in the whole complicated network of metabolism.

This sort of organisation of life may, in some ways, be compared with the organisation of a musical work, such as a symphony, the actual existence of which depends on determinate sequences and concordances of individual sounds. One has only to disturb the sequence and the symphony as such will be destroyed, only disharmony and chaos will remain.

In a similar way, the organisation of life is fundamentally dependent on a regular sequence of metabolic reactions and the form and structure of living bodies are flowing in nature. For this reason organisms can only exist for any length of time as a result of the continuous accomplishment of chemical transformations, which constitute the essence of living, and the cessation of which would lead to the disruption of the living system and the death of the organism.

In contrast to this, the basic structure of the machine is static. When the machine is working, only the energy source or fuel undergoes chemical change, while the actual structure remains materially unchanged irrespective of whether it is made of metal or of plastic, and the less it is changed (by corrosion for example) the longer the actual machine will last.

Thus, the actual principle of stability which enables them to exist for a prolonged period is different for organisms and machines. The similarities between them which have been enumerated above are, therefore, only very superficial and, when examined in more detail, they are seen to be purely formal.

We may demonstrate this in the particular case of mechanical movement by an organism. In the muscles of the animal carrying out this movement, the protein fibrils are orientated in a particular way relative to one another. Such a structure, however, cannot be likened in any way to that of a machine. In a machine the structural elements do not play any part whatsoever in the chemical transformation of the energy source. If the component parts of the machine were themselves to undergo chemical transformation during their work, this would, of course, lead quickly to the destruction of the whole mechanism. On the other hand, the elements of construction of the living body, the protein fibrils in this case, themselves take a direct part in the metabolic reactions which serve as the source of that energy which is transformed into mechanical movement. The same may also be said of the comparison of organisms with heat engines in respect of energetics. We now know that the analogy between respiration and combustion is very formal. In combustion the surmounting of the energy of activation, which is necessary for the accomplishment of the oxidative reactions, is done by raising the temperature considerably, whereas in respiration this is not needed. Respiration is based on an enzymic lowering of the energy of activation.

If the transformation of energy took place in the same way in organisms as it does in heat engines, then, at temperatures at which living things can exist, the coefficient of their useful activity would fall to an insignificant fraction of one per cent. It is, in fact, amazingly high, considerably higher than that obtained in present-day heat engines. The explanation of this is that the oxidation of sugar, or any other respiratory fuel, in the organism takes place not as a single chemical act, but by a series of individual reactions co-ordinated in time.

If the oxidation of organic materials in the organism took place suddenly, then the living body would be unable to make rational use of all the energy set free in this way, especially if it was given off in the form of heat. In the oxidation of only 1 mole (180 g.) of sugar about 700 kcal. are liberated. The instantaneous liberation of this amount of energy would be associated with a sharp rise in temperature, the denaturation of proteins and the destruction of the living body. This same energy effect, which is brought about by the organism under ordinary conditions of low temperature, depends on the fact that in the process of biological oxidation, sugar is not converted into carbon dioxide and water suddenly, but slowly, by stages. A process of this sort not only gives the possibility of surmounting the energy of activation at ordinary temperatures, it also enables the living body to make rational use of the energy which is gradually set free. Thus, the more highly organised the metabolism, i.e., the better the co-ordination between the separate reactions comprising it, the higher the coefficient of useful activity.

The principle of evaluating nutrients simply in terms of their content of calories led to many difficulties in its practical application. This principle was only overthrown with great difficulty, as a result of studies of vitamins and essential amino acids, and investigations which showed that, unlike a heat engine, there occurs in the organisms, not only oxidation of energy-providing material, but also transformation of the fundamental protein structures of the living body, which are broken down and resynthesised in the general interaction of the organism with the external medium.

Finally, it must be pointed out that the ways of 'overcoming entropy' used by organisms and contemporary mechanisms or automats also differ from one another in principle. As we have shown above, organisms manage to avoid 'thermodynamic equilibrium' just because they are open or flowing systems. Recent studies of the thermodynamics of such systems have shown them to be essentially different from classical thermodynamics, which is based on the phenomena observed in closed systems. It gives us a perfectly rational explanation of why it is that, in organisms, entropy not only does not increase, but may even decrease.

According to Wiener, a different principle underlies the ability of contemporary cybernetic automats to counteract the tendency to the increase of entropy and to create zones of organisation around themselves. In order to explain this ability, Wiener uses the same idea as Maxwell used in the form of his demons. According to present-day ideas, however, this 'Maxwell's demon' has to be continually obtaining 'information' according to which he opens or closes the doors to molecules of high or low rates of movement. For a number of years the overriding wish to identify the organism with a mechanism forced many scientists to ignore all the increasing factual evidence and look for some rigid, unchanging, static structures in the living body so that these structures themselves might be regarded as the specific bearers of life.

At the end of last century it was widely held among

biologists that the organisation of protoplasm was based on the presence in it of a certain machine-like structure formed of solid and unchanging ' beams and braces ' interlacing with one another. It was thought that the only thing that prevented us from seeing this structure was the imperfection of our optical methods.

As these methods developed, however, the search for static, ' life-determining ' structures was first transferred to the realm of colloid chemical formations and then to the realm of intramolecular structure. In this way there arose the concept that the material carriers of life are to be found in the single molecules of heritable substance which have a static, unchanging structure and form a part of the nuclear chromosomes. This concept is associated with the work of T. Morgan and his followers concerning the gene nature of life. According to H. Muller the " living gene molecule " can only undergo change in detail but is essentially so static that it has maintained its internal life-determining structure unchanged throughout the whole development of life on the Earth. This concept of the Morgan school of geneticists was fully expressed in Schroedinger's well-known book *What is Life?* Schroedinger saw the key to the understanding of life in the fact that the structure which is the only one natural and peculiar to life, namely that of the gene, " is so long-lasting and constant as to border on the miraculous ". It is as unchanging as though it were frozen. Thus, according to Schroedinger, the organisa-tion of life is based upon the principle of ' clockwork ', the structure of which remains completely constant at room temperature as well as at absolute zero. In his conclusion Schroedinger writes " Now, I think, few words more are needed to disclose the point of resemblance between a clock-work and an organism. It is simply and solely that the latter also hinges upon a solid—the aperiodic crystal forming the hereditary substance, largely withdrawn from the disorder of heat motion."

The only new thing that has been added to the gene theory up to now is that an attempt has been made to give a chemical reality to the previously rather vague idea of the gene molecule in the form of a suggestion that the living molecule may be a particle of nuclear nucleoprotein or, according to the latest evidence, simply the molecule of desoxyribonucleic acid.   It would seem that everything else in the cell is to be regarded as merely the medium for the ' living molecule '.

From this point of view the capacity for self-reproduction, which is characteristic of living things, is based only on the strictly determinate, static, intramolecular structure of desoxyribonucleic acid (DNA), on the specific arrangement of purine pyrimidine mononucleotide residues in the polynucleotide chain of DNA.   This arrangement represents, in the terminology of cybernetics, the code in which the whole collection of specific characteristics of the living body is stored.   The transfer of ' hereditary information' may thus be thought of as something like the work of a stamping machine in which the molecule of DNA represents the matrix which always reproduces a single uniform structure.   Such hypotheses are very impressive to the protagonists of the machine theory of life and are therefore very widely supported by contemporary physicists as well as biologists.   We shall go into this in more detail in the course of further explanation.   All that is needed now is to remark briefly on the present state of the problem.   The more concrete the biochemical studies of the self-reproduction of living things, the more obvious it becomes that the process is not just bound up with this or that particular substance or a single molecule of it, but is determined by the whole system of organisation of the living body which, as we have seen, is flowing in nature and is in no way to be compared with a stamping machine with an unchanging matrix.   Speaking on this subject at the 4th International Congress of Biochemistry, E. Chargaff said " It is even possible that we may be dealing with templates in time rather than in space ", by which he meant a definite order in which processes occur in the living thing.   In any case when we are not making a formal comparison between the phenomena occurring in living beings and those occurring in machines, but are trying to understand what they are really like, we find, not only similarities, but also a profound difference between the two kinds of system.   This difference is not merely fortuitous but forms the very essence of their organisation.

In the first place, it is connected with the fact that the ' purpose ' which inspires a person to create some machine which is necessary to him has nothing in common with the task of self-preservation and self-reproduction which determines the organisation of living things. The aims in constructing a watch, a steam locomotive or an automatic device for defence against aerial attack are to tell the time correctly, to transport people and goods and effectively to bring down enemy aircraft. Owing to our present ways of thinking and technical habits which have evolved over many centuries we find it far easier to solve these problems rationally by building static structures out of metal or some solid plastic material, and this is what, in fact, we do.

In this way the actual principles of construction of any machine now in existence reflect the character of the person who made it, his intellectual and technological level, his aims and his methods of solving the problems in front of him.

This also applies fully to the various 'cybernetic toys' which are now being made, the point of which is simply to imitate living things, such as Grey Walter's 'tortoise', Shannon's ' mouse ', Ducrocq's ' fox ' and Ashby's ' homeostat ', constructions which have been wittily described by Grey Walter as "machines which can serve no useful purpose". The structure of all these necessarily carries the predetermination put there by those who constructed them and P. Cossa was quite right when, in his book, *La cybernétique* (Paris, 1957), he wrote of them as follows:—

" What is inherent in the living thing (adaptability), is not merely the means but the end itself: the preservation of life, the preservation of the continuity of existence by adaptation to the environment. There is nothing like this in the homeostat, it has no inherent ultimate aim. If a living thing, which has had its equilibrium upset, perseveringly tries out, one after another, all possible means of adapting itself to its new environment, this is explained as an effort to survive. If the homeostat tries out its 390625 combinations one after another it only does so because that is what Ashby wanted of it."*

Of course one may imagine machines of the future which will imitate living things very closely; machines designed as flowing systems in which energy is used by easy stages; they might even be able to reproduce themselves etc. All the same,

* Retranslation from Russian. A. S.

the organisation of these machines would still reflect the specific task which those who made them had set themselves; they would always bear the marks of their origins.

The insuperable difference in principle between machines and organisms stands out specially clearly when we consider the question of the origin of individual systems. We know that, in its general organisation in which the structure is adapted to the performance of particular tasks, a machine develops first in the mind of its creator and not as a real physical system. This idea is then expressed in drawings or plans. These plans usually form the basis for the construction of individual components in accordance with their specifications. These are then assembled and it is only at this stage that the machine appears as a physical object.

The way in which a machine arises is, thus, perfectly clear, but if we try to solve the problem of the origin of living things by analogy with machines, we shall, logically and inevitably, reach an idealistic conclusion.

The book by Schroedinger, which has already been quoted, may serve as a good example of this. In it the author set out to understand life from the point of view of physics, that is, on a purely materialist basis. Nevertheless, in his conclusion, he was forced to characterise life as " the finest masterpiece ever achieved along the lines of the Lord's quantum mechanics", i.e. to put it plainly, he acknowledged the divine origin of life.

There is a difference in form, but not in substance, between this conclusion and those of other attempts to solve the problem of the origin of life which have been made on the basis of purely mechanistic assumptions as to its genetic nature (e.g. those of A. Dauvillier, G. Blum, L. Roka and others). Essentially all these attempts arrive at the same explanation. In the primitive and, as yet, lifeless solution of organic material there somehow arose particles of protein, nucleic acid or nucleoprotein and these, suddenly, on their appearance, had an intramolecular structure which was extremely well adapted to the accomplishment of self-reproduction and other vital functions. Thus, there arose the ' primary living matrix ' which could later be elaborated, but the ' purposive ' life-determining structure was not necessarily immediately the same as it is to-day. The question then arises as to what were the natural laws underlying the origin of an intramolecular structure which was adapted to the performance of specific functions. Iron can exist in the elementary form in inorganic nature and, under certain circumstances, may take the form of shapeless lumps, but, as Aristotle wrote, even a sword cannot arise in this way without human intervention, for its structure is suited to the accomplishment of a particular end. In just the same way (as we shall see later) those physical and chemical laws, which were the only ones prevailing in the waters of the primaeval ocean, were quite enough to account for the primary formation, in those waters, of high-molecular protein-like polymers and polynucleotides with a more or less irregular arrangement of mononucleotide residues. By themselves, however, these laws are quite insufficient to provide for the possibility of the development of any structures adapted to the performance of particular functions. The supporters of these hypotheses ' explain ' so to speak, the functional suitability of the structures of their primary matrices as being due to ' a lucky chance ' or ' just pure chance ', in which Dauvillier is justified in seeing ' the hand of an eccentric creator '. This ' hand ' does not differ essentially from Schroedinger's ' the Lord's quantum mechanics ' nor even from St. Augustine's ' divine will '.

In his book, the English edition of which bears the most intriguing title, *The Origins of Life*, A. Ducrocq claims to have given a general explanation of life and its origins based on ' cybernetic theory ' and to have demonstrated the laws of the delicate interaction of forces whereby " conglomerates of atoms are transformed into living aggregates " i.e. living things. On closer acquaintance with this book, however, we find that, in the last analysis, the whole thing amounts to a statement that the chain of DNA, which served as the point of origin for the whole series of living things and which was constructed in a specific way, must have appeared in some improbable way in the solution of organic substances, for its appearance " had a probability which was not nil ". In what way is this different from those numerous hypotheses, which we have already mentioned, about the chance origin of life ?

Physicists assert that, in principle, it is possible that, by chance, the table on which I am writing might rise up of its own accord into the air owing to the simultaneous orientation of the thermal movement of all its molecules in the same direction. It is hardly likely, however, that anyone would conduct his experimental work, or his practical activities in general, with this possibility in view. Furthermore, the experimental scientist attaches value to those theories which open up possibilities for investigation, but how can one study a phenomenon which, at the best, could only occur once in the whole time of the existence of the Earth? The conception of the chance origin of the ' living molecule ' is, therefore, completely fruitless from a practical point of view and, as we shall see later, it is also theoretically unsound.

There can be no doubt that the conscious or unconscious attempts to liken the origin of living things to the assembly of a machine also lies at the root of the many contemporary statements to the effect that, in the original solution of organic substances, there were formed various substances which were at once structurally suitable and well adapted to the carrying out of particular vital functions and then, by their combination, they gave rise to the first living body, just as a machine is assembled from separate components the structure of which was already adapted to doing a particular job.

According to these statements the first thing that happened, even before the appearance of the most primitive organism, was the formation of protein-enzymes with their strictly determinate intramolecular structures and their very efficient adaptation to the carrying out of particular catalytic reactions which are very important in metabolism, nucleic acids, which play an essential part in the process of reproduction of organisms and other compounds which are to be found in the very efficient ' rationally constructed ' organs of living protoplasm as we know it, though this itself only arose secondarily by the combination of the primary compounds.

Such an idea reminds one of the sayings of the ancient Greek philosopher Empedocles who believed that, when living things originally came into being, individual organs were first formed independently of one another—" Thus there grew up a multitude of heads without necks, naked arms wandered around without their shoulders and eyes moved about with no foreheads." Later these unmatched members joined together and in this way the various sorts of animals and people were formed.

IT IS ONLY POSSIBLE TO UNDERSTAND LIFE BY STUDYING ITS ORIGIN AND DEVELOPMENT

From the modern Darwinian point of view the falsity, not to say absurdity, of such a theory is perfectly obvious. Any particular organ can only originate and become perfected as part of the evolutionary development of the organism as a whole.

The specialised and complicated structure of the eye and the hand are adapted to their purpose only when considered in relation to the functions which they carry out. It is impossible, even unthinkable, to take seriously the evolution of an individual organ such as the Empedoclean ' eyes with no foreheads ' because the very functions which determined their structure would have no meaning under those circumstances. The action of natural selection can, therefore, only affect them as parts of whole living things.

In just the same way enzymes, nucleic acids and so on are only parts of the living body, they are like organs, subserving definite, vitally necessary functions. Thus the catalytic activity of enzymes or the specific functions of nucleic acids are of no importance to the substances themselves but are only important to the whole living body in which the particular metabolic reactions take place. It follows that, when not a part of such a body, before its formation, they would be quite unable to acquire a ' purposive ' structure, suited to carrying out their vital functions. It is quite natural and right to suppose that there were successive developments proceeding from simpler to more complicated systems, but, although the individual organs are simpler than the whole organism, we should not be like Empedocles and imagine that animals and people arose by the fusion of individual organs.

Darwin showed the true way in which higher organisms have arisen by the evolution of lower living things which were more simply organised but were still complete systems in themselves.

Similarly it would be wrong to suppose that, in the organically rich waters of the primaeval ocean, there arose proteins and nucleic acids with a ' purposive ' structure extremely accurately and well adapted to the carrying out of particular biological functions and that, later, by their combination, the living body itself was created.

All that we can expect from the action of the laws of physics and chemistry, which were the only ones on the still lifeless Earth, is that there were formed more or less randomly constructed polymers with a haphazard distribution of peptides and mononucleotides and thus having no ' purposiveness ' or adaptation to the carrying out of particular functions.

These polymers could, however, join together with one another to form complete multimolecular systems though, naturally, these were incomparably simpler than living bodies. It was only as a result of the prolonged evolution of these original systems, their interaction with their environment and their natural selection, that there arose those forms of organisation which are peculiar to the living body, namely metabolism, and with it proteins, enzymes, nucleic acids and those other complicated and ' purposefully ' constructed substances which are characteristic of contemporary organisms.   Thus there is not even the most remote similarity between the origin of life and the assembly of a machine.

These two sorts of system show a likeness to each other only if we consider them in their finished state, divorced from their origins.   Once we start to deal with this question the difference between the machine and the organism immediately becomes apparent and it is obvious that the two kinds of system are essentially of a different quality.

This concept is understandable and even simple, for the origin of life and the origin of the machine took place at very widely separated levels of evolutionary development.

We may note the following important stages in this development from the moment of the formation of the Earth to the present day.   For the first milliards of years of its existence our planet had no life on it and all the processes occurring on it were subject only to the laws of physics and chemistry. This stage of development may be referred to as inorganic or abiogenic. Life then arose on the Earth and a new biological stage of evolution began. Now new biological laws were added to the old physical and chemical ones and these new laws have now come to the fore and assumed an ever-growing importance in the progressive development of living things. The crowning achievement of this period was the emergence of man heralding the beginning of the third or social stage of evolution. Now even the biological laws have been driven from the foreground and the laws of development of human society have begun to play the leading part in further progress.

It is very important that, with the beginning of each new stage of development, with the origin of a new form of the movement of matter, the tempo of its evolution increases. The abiogenic period of the existence of the Earth lasted for thousands of millions of years, but the decisive progress of biological evolution only required hundreds or perhaps even tens of millions of years for its accomplishment. The whole development of mankind has only lasted a million years. Social transformations have occurred within thousands of years or even centuries and now we can easily notice substantial changes in human society over periods reckoned in decades.

There can hardly have been any significant biological change in the human race since the time of Aristotle, but it is only during the last few hundred years that man has attained hitherto unimaginable power over his environment. He can cover the ground faster than any deer, swim beneath the water better than any fish and fly through the air incomparably faster and further than any bird. But this is not because he has grown wings or fins and gills during that time. The powers acquired by mankind are not the result of biological but of social development. In particular, machines, which play such an outstanding part in man's conquest of the forces of nature are the fruit of this development, for man could only create them by all-round mastery of the experiences accumulated by his forebears over many centuries, only, in fact, on the basis of the communal life of mankind.

Thus machines are not merely inorganic systems operating in accordance with no laws other than those of physics and chemistry. They are, in origin, not biological but higher, i.e. social forms of the motion of matter. We can therefore only understand their real nature through studying their origin. We shall now discuss some other examples so that this may become clearer to the reader.

On the banks of great rivers, which have worn down thick sedimentary formations, one may find stones made of calcite which are commonly called ' devil's fingers ' because of their queer shape, which certainly does remind one of the shape of a finger except that it is sharpened at one end into a cone. In old times people believed that these objects were formed by lightning striking sand and even their scientific name— belemnites—is derived from this supposition as to their origin. If this were the case they should always be associated with mineral formations of the abiogenic, inorganic world. In fact, however, it has been shown that belemnites are the fossilised remains of rostra, which are parts of the insides of molluscs, and that these are characteristic of a particular group of cephalopod molluscs which lived in the Jurassic and Cretaceous periods and were completely extinct by the beginning of the Tertiary period. On the surface of some belemnites one may even find traces of the blood vessels of the mantle, or soft envelope, of the body of the mollusc which once enclosed the belemnite. Thus belemnites, taken on their own without reference to their origin, are clearly completely lacking in life. From the point of view of their chemical composition and also from that of their characteristic physical properties they appear to be objects of the inorganic world. Belemnites, however, could not be formed in that world as a result of the elementary forces of inorganic nature alone. For this reason we cannot understand the essential nature of these objects if we do not know about their biological origin or the history of the development of life on the Earth. In that case they would certainly seem to us to be some miraculous ' devil's fingers '.

I will now ask my readers to let me indulge in fantasy as this will enable me to present my ideas more clearly.

Let us imagine that people have succeeded in making automatic machines or robots which can not only carry out a lot of work for mankind but can even independently create the energetic conditions necessary for their work, obtain metals and use them to construct components, and from these build new robots like themselves. Then some terrible disaster happened on the Earth, and it destroyed not only all the people but all living things on our planet. The metallic robots, however, remained. They continued to build others like themselves and so, although the old mechanisms gradually wore out, new ones arose and the ' race ' of robots continued and even, perhaps, increased within limits.

Let us further imagine that all this has already happened on one of the planets of our solar system, on Mars, for example, and that we have landed on that planet. On its waterless and lifeless expanses we suddenly meet with the robots. Do we have to regard them as living inhabitants of the planet? Of course not. The robots will not represent life but something else. Maybe a very complicated and efficient form of the organisation and movement of matter, but still different from life. They are analogous to the belemnites which we have already considered, the only difference being that the belemnites arose in the process of biological development while the robots were based on the higher, social form of the motion of matter.

Life existed in the Jurassic sea and the rostra of cephalopod molluscs played a particular part in it. The life vanished and the belemnites remained, but now they appear to be lifeless objects of the inorganic world. Similarly, automatic machines and, in particular, our imaginary robots, could only develop as offshoots of human (or some similar) society, as the fruit of the social form of organisation and movement of matter, and they have played a considerable part in the development of that form of organisation. But that form was destroyed, it vanished and the robots are on their own, not controlled by it. They are completely subject to the laws of physics and chemistry alone.

Nevertheless, just as one cannot understand what a belemnite is if one has no knowledge of life, so it is impossible to grasp the nature of the ' Martian robot ' without a sufficient acquaintance with the social form of the motion of matter which gave rise to it. This would be true even if one were able to take down the robot into its individual components and reassemble it correctly. Even then there would remain hidden from our understanding those features of the organisation of the robot which were purposefully constructed for the solution of problems which those who built them envisaged at some time, but which are completely unknown to us.

When the Lilliputians found a watch in Gulliver's pocket they were not in a state to understand its nature properly, although, according to Swift, the Lilliputians had a very extensive knowledge of mathematics and mechanics. After prolonged deliberation they decided that it was a pocket god which Gulliver consulted each time he started to do something.

If some ' thinking Martian ' were to chance on a watch flying about somewhere in space perhaps he too would be able to take it to pieces and put it together again but there would still be a lot about it that would be incomprehensible to him. And not only will the Martians not understand, but many of my readers will probably not be able to explain why there are only twelve numbers on the faces of ordinary clocks although the day is divided into twenty-four hours. This question can only be answered from a good knowledge of the history of human culture and, in particular, of the history of watchmaking.

Similarly, an understanding of the nature of life is impossible without a knowledge of the history of its origin. Usually, however, the nature and origin of life have been regarded, and are even now regarded, as being two completely separate problems. Thus, at the end of last century and the beginning of the present one the problem of the origin of life was denounced as an accursed and insoluble problem, work on which was unworthy of a serious scientist and was a pure waste of time. People tried to achieve an understanding of the nature of life, which is the main problem of biology at present, primarily in a purely metaphysical way, completely isolated from its origin. In principle this amounts to their wanting, crudely speaking, to take the living body apart into its component screws and wheels like a watch and then to try to put it together again.

Even Mephistopheles jeered at such an approach in his advice to the young scholar.

> " Wer will was Lebendigs erkennen und beschreiben,
>   Sucht erst den Geist herauszutreiben,
>   Dann hat er die Teile in seiner Hand,
>   Fehlt leider! nur das geistige Band.
>   *Encheiresin naturae* nennt's die Chemie,
>   Spottet ihrer selbst, und weiss nicht wie." *

Of course, a detailed analysis of the substances and phenomena peculiar to contemporary living things is extremely important and absolutely necessary for an understanding of life. That is beyond doubt. The whole question is whether this, by itself, is enough for such an understanding. It is clearly not. Even now, for all our skill in this sort of analysis, we are still very far from being able to point to any way in which life could actually be synthesised although we admit that this synthesis is theoretically perfectly possible.

This is by no means merely because our analysis has, as yet, not been finished, that we still have not found out all the details of the structure of the living body.

" The whole ", wrote M. Planck, " is always somewhat different from the sum of the separate parts." It is only possible to understand this whole by knowing it in its maturity and in its development, by studying and reproducing the processes of gradual elaboration and perfection of the more primitive systems which were its precursors.

It is now becoming more and more obvious that a knowledge of the essential nature of life is only possible through a knowledge of its origin. Now, too, this origin no longer seems so puzzling as it did not long ago. We are sketching out in more and more detail the actual ways in which life arose on the Earth. It could only have happened as an integral part of the general historic development of our planet. The facts

---

* Whoso would describe and know aught that's alive
  Seeks first the spirit forth to drive;
  The parts he then hath in his hand,
  But lacks, alas! the spirit-band.
  Encheiresin naturae chemists call it now,
  Mock at themselves and know not how.

               Trans. W. H. van der Smissen

at our disposal indicate that the origin of life was a gradual process in which organic substances became more and more complicated and formed complete systems which were in a state of continual interaction with the medium surrounding them.

Following the path of the emergence of life in this way we encounter neither the ' almighty hand of the Creator ' nor machines which made their appearance at a far later stage in the development of matter. We do, however, discover in this way how and why it is that the particular original systems which existed were transformed, in the process of evolution, into those which are characteristic of life instead of into others and how, in that same process of the establishment of life, there arose new biological laws which had not existed before, and also how the ' purposiveness ' which we notice in all living things came into being.

In this way our knowledge gives us a real understanding of the essential organisation of the most primitive forms of life and, on that basis, we can easily follow the further evolution of these forms by applying the precepts of evolutionary theory. We can trace the formation of new features characteristic of highly organised living beings, including man, who is the culmination of the biological stage of the development of matter.

Thus we arrive at the main idea underlying this book which had already been formulated by Heraclitus of Ephesus and was included in the works of Aristotle:—" One can only understand the essence of things when one knows their origin and development."

CHAPTER II

THE ORIGIN OF LIFE

CONTEMPORARY COSMOGONIC THEORIES

W E live in a world which is continually developing and evolving without interruption. The development is an irreversible process. Evolution is, therefore, often likened to the ' arrow of time ', flying in one direction only. In the light of what we now know, however, this picture must be considered old-fashioned. The speed of an arrow is always decreasing. The speed of evolution, on the other hand, is, as we saw in the previous chapter, ever increasing. It would therefore be better to compare it with a space rocket which increases its speed by stages.

Similarly, when a new form of the organisation and motion of matter arises in the course of evolution, the tempo of evolution increases sharply as though by a new and powerful thrust. When this happens, however, the acceleration affects a more and more limited section of the evolving matter.

Thus, with the origin of life, the biosphere was quickly developed but it only represented a small part of the whole planet. With the origin of man there was a further acceleration of tempo and human society was developed, though this only constituted a small fraction of the whole aggregate of living things.

The origin of life was an integral part of the general evolutionary development of our world. It can therefore only be profitably studied against the background of that general development of matter. To avoid being too diffuse in our further exposition we shall, however, concentrate on those objects which played a direct part in the transition from the non-living to the living state, gradually narrowing down the circle of our interest.

As early as the 18th century W. Herschel put forward the ingenious idea, later supported by Laplace, that if stars and constellations are not unchanging, then they originated at different times and are still originating; a process of gradual development then takes place and we can see the various stages of it in the sky.

For a long time this idea was neglected by astronomers and it was only at the beginning of this century that it was revived in connection with the construction of the Hertzsprung-Russell stellar diagram. This diagram shows the relationship between the spectral types of stars (i.e. the temperatures of their surfaces) and their absolute brightness or luminosity which expresses the total amount of energy given out by a star over a given period of time. The abscissa of the diagram represents the absolute temperature decreasing from 30,000° C. on the left to 2500° C. on the right. The ordinate represents the absolute brightness of the stars, that of the Sun being the unit. Plotted in this way the dots representing all the known stars form a group in the diagram occupying fairly narrow bands or lines. The main one of these lies diagonally across the diagram from its left upper corner downwards and towards the right.

The overwhelming majority (about 95 per cent.) of stars which have been observed, including the Sun, are represented by points which lie on this diagonal, which is usually referred to as the 'main stellar sequence'. Such a distribution of stellar characteristics is, of course, not accidental. One of the authors of the diagram, H. Russell, attributed a directly evolutionary significance to it. He suggested that each star, in the course of its individual development, proceeded in some manner along the line of the diagram. Cosmogonists have still not reached unanimity as to the actual way in which this stellar evolution takes place. It would seem that different stars develop in different ways but the actual idea that fresh stars are constantly being formed and successively developing has now acquired a very solid basis in a number of astronomic facts which have been established recently. In this connection the work of V. Ambartsumyan on stellar associations is of great interest.

These associations are unstable because the mutual attraction of the stars comprising them is weaker than their attraction to the galaxy, especially to its central part. The stars forming these associations are therefore flying apart in different directions and, according to Ambartsumyan's calculations, such associations cannot last for much longer than some tens of millions of years. Since we can see them now, however, the associations and the stars composing them must have been

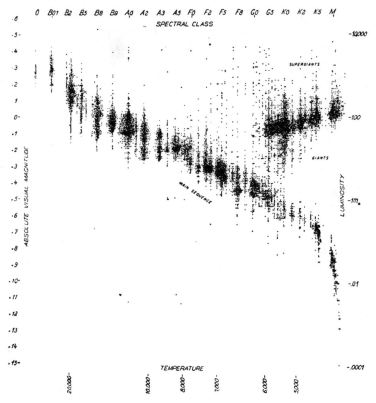

Fig. 1. Curve of the main sequence (Hertzsprung-Russell diagram).

formed relatively recently. Thus it shows that the process of star formation is still going on.

As well as this there must have been formed and still be forming planetary systems like our own solar system. Evidence obtained recently, in particular the studies of E. Holmberg, shows that systems of this sort are widely distributed in the universe; that stars surrounded by relatively small cold bodies are rather the rule than the rare exception, as was believed twenty years ago. In this connection, the majority of contemporary astronomers and cosmogonists consider that our planetary system is not the result of any very rare 'lucky chance' but that it developed, like many similar systems, as a quite normal phenomenon, as a stage in the consecutive development of matter. It became more and more obvious that one cannot regard the problem of the evolution of a planetary system in isolation from the general problem of the origin of stars and that the two phenomena are merely two successive stages in the single process of evolution of cosmic bodies.

THE ORIGIN OF THE SOLAR SYSTEM

It is now considered most likely that the process of development of stars and planets is in some way associated with the evolution of the matter of the interstellar gas and dust. As is now well known, by no means all the matter in the Galaxy (and other analogous systems) is concentrated into those large aggregates which are the stars and planets. A considerable part of its mass is distributed through space in the form of very diffuse gas and dust. Clouds of cosmic dust are mainly concentrated in the middle of the galaxy. Some of them we can even see with the naked eye, sharply defined in the form of dark, irregularly shaped areas against the light background of the Milky Way. This is because the collections of dust obscure the light of the stars lying behind them (fig. 2).†

It has been established, by many recent observations, that these accumulations of dust and gas may attain tremendous sizes, 200 parsecs* or even more, and their mass may be greater than 300 times that of the Sun. As well as these gigantic clouds, it was discovered ten years ago that there are comparatively small clouds of cosmic gas and dust which can easily be seen against the background of a nebula as they are extremely opaque. They take the form of circular, or nearly circular spots and are therefore called 'globules'. The smallest globule known at present has a diameter of 0·006 parsecs and a mass 500 times less than that of the Sun. Other globules have a greater mass ; sometimes they are several times as

---

* The parsec is a unit of length used in astronomy. 1 parsec = 3·26 light years or 3·08 × 10^{13}Km.

†Figure 2 follows page 52.

great as the Sun. Thus, such a globule may contain enough matter to serve for the formation of one or several stars. The extremely high density of the globules has led scientists to consider the possibility that stars originated in this way. The density of the globules is thousands of times that of the inter-stellar medium which surrounds them.

Contemporary cosmogonists are rather inclined to hold the view that one such globule was the ' protostar ' from which our planetary system was formed. At some stage in the development of the globule a massive central body was formed in it and this grew quickly by attracting the particles of the matter of the globule towards itself. By doing so it soon grew dense and its internal temperature therefore rose higher and higher. When the central body reached a mass comparable with that of the Sun, conditions within it became favourable for the setting up of a cycle of nuclear reactions similar to that which occurs when a hydrogen bomb explodes. The hydrogen, which formed the greater part of the mass of the central body, began to be transformed into helium and this was associated with the liberation of enormous amounts of intra-atomic energy. The temperature of the central body quickly rose to many millions of degrees centigrade and it became a spontaneously shining star, it became, in fact, our Sun. Its further development followed the line of the main sequence of the Hertzsprung-Russell diagram.

The rest of the material of the globule, which did not take part in the formation of the Sun, formed itself at the same time into a discoidal cloud of gas and dust and gave rise to the ' protoplanets '.

In the cosmogonic literature of the present day we find a large number of hypotheses which attempt to explain the mechanism of the formation of planets. The cosmogonists invoke turbulent movement, gravitational forces and the physical forces which develop when particles of gas and dust collide with one another. The movement of these particles in the primary planetary cloud must have been rather chaotic. The particles revolved independently of one another around the central body as very small satellites. They could move in different directions and in different planes. In doing so they inevitably collided with one another. However, as the interaction of the heavy particles or the collision of specks of dust or molecules of gas was inelastic and consequently was accompanied by the transformation of kinetic energy into other forms of energy the total amount of mechanical energy in the planetary cloud decreased in the course of time. Mathematical analysis of the whole process shows that this sort of development of the planetary cloud would necessarily lead to its gradual flattening, to its assuming a discoidal form with all the particles in it moving in more or less the same plane. Furthermore, a process of concentration would inevitably start in the cloud, with gradual aggregation of the scattered material, first into comparatively small bodies (planetesimals) and then into larger formations which became centres for the aggregation of the material which, in the long run, led to the formation of planets.

Most present-day cosmogonists base themselves on the simplest physical and chemical laws and try to derive, by suitable mathematical calculations, a rational explanation of the peculiarities of structure present in our solar system: the regularity of the motion of the planets and their satellites, the form of their orbits, the distances between the planets, the dimensions and masses of the planets, the distribution of angular momentum between the Sun and the planets etc.

Agreement of results derived theoretically with those observed directly is usually regarded as a criterion of the correctness of the hypothesis concerned. Moreover, contemporary cosmogonic hypotheses must not contradict the numerous geological, geophysical and geochemical facts now known.

Unfortunately there is scarcely one of the present hypotheses as to the origin of the planetary system which would fulfil all these requirements. Another circumstance which makes it far more difficult to solve our problem is that we have more or less detailed factual data about only one solar system, our own. We are therefore forced to consider the origin and development of objects of which only one single example is available for our direct study and it is hard for us to decide which aspects of it are common to and typical of any planetary system and which are merely peculiar or accidental. In view of this, planetary cosmogony cannot yet be held to be properly worked out.

However, if we base ourselves on a comparison of the results obtained from planetary cosmogony with the results of geophysical and geochemical investigations, it is already possible for us to put forward some sort of hypothesis as to both the chemical composition of the surface of the Earth and as to the physical conditions prevailing there at the time when the Earth had already been formed into a planet but when life had not yet developed on it.

For our purposes, naturally, we should concentrate special attention on those elements which later entered into the composition of living bodies, and their chemical compounds.

THE FORMATION OF THE CRUST OF THE EARTH

In the previous chapter we have shown how extremely important the chemical characteristics of living bodies are for an understanding of the essential nature of life. We must understand the nature of the chemical compounds which form the material substrate of life. However, for such an understanding we do not merely need a detailed physical and chemical analysis of the living substrate in the form in which it exists at present. We also require a knowledge of the ways in which it was formed under natural conditions during the process of development of our planet, when the original and extremely primitive compounds gradually, and in accordance with physical and chemical laws, changed and became more complicated, assuming more and more new properties. Only if we can make studies of this sort shall we be in a state to know why it is these particular compounds and not some other ones which now take the leading place in the structure of living matter and why it is that, in the life of all the organisms known to us, it is these particular chemical and physical processes which go on and not other possible ones. For an understanding of the essential nature of life this may well be no less important than a simple knowledge of what is happening in living things now and how it is happening.

Organic substances form the basis of all the multitude of contemporary organisms. Without them there is no life for it is only their regular interaction that can produce the conditions for the dynamic organisation of living bodies in time, which is the essence of biological metabolism. Hence we can see why we have to begin our study of the problem of the origin of life on the Earth by studying the ways in which organic substances were formed primarily, under natural conditions. In our efforts to solve our problem we may, however, turn to the study of these conditions in their present form and then we shall be faced with a great, and, at first glance, insuperable difficulty. It is this. On the surface of the Earth at the present stage of its development the only way in which biologically important organic compounds are formed is by living creatures. They are only formed as a result of a very highly developed, organised, vital process.

Almost all organic material is now produced by photosynthesis. Green plants use the energy of sunlight and absorb carbon dioxide from the air. From this inorganic form of carbon they thus create all the organic substances necessary for their life and growth. Animals obtain these substances from plants either by eating them as such or by feeding on vegetarian creatures or on their corpses or remains. Similar nutritional expedients also serve as sources of inorganic food for most colourless micro-organisms and only a few of them can form organic compounds on their own behalf by chemosynthesis which, like photosynthesis, is a biological process.

The whole living population of the Earth thus lives at the expense of the organic compounds which are formed biogenically in the course of the vital processes of a proportion of organisms. Not only is this so, but even the mineral organic substances, petroleum and coal, are also essentially biogenic in origin in that they are, for the most part, products of the far-reaching decomposition and transformation of the residues of past organisms which have become buried in the crust of the Earth.

On these grounds many scientists of the earlier part of this century reached the conclusion that, in general, organic substances could only be formed under natural conditions by the activity of organisms (biogenically).

The fact that such substances can now be artificially synthesised by man did not seem to these scientists to contradict their view, for man is also a living thing. He sets going a sequence of chemical reactions such as take place in organisms but are absent from the inorganic world. (*Cf.* especially Reinke's pronouncements on this question.)

Such an assumption, of course, seemed to place an insuperable difficulty in the way of solving the problem of the origin of life. One must suppose that living things arose as a result of the evolution of the organic substances of which they are made up. If, however, these substances can only be formed under natural conditions in the course of the vital activities of organisms, we are forced willy nilly into a vicious circle from which there is no escape. However, this difficulty only arises if we assume that the Earth was always the same as it is at present.

If, on the other hand, we try to approach the problem in a less parochial way and consider it in relation to what we know of conditions outside our own planet, on other heavenly bodies, we shall arrive at a different conclusion.

It is now well known that the simplest organic compounds, namely the hydrocarbons and their nearest derivatives, are to be found on almost all of the heavenly bodies which are accessible to study, and in most of these places they must have arisen without the slightest connection with life, under conditions which absolutely preclude biogenesis. In particular, it has been established that compounds of carbon and hydrogen are present in the incandescent atmospheres of many stars including the Sun, in the cold clouds of gas and dust of interstellar space, on the surfaces of the larger planets and their satellites, in the substance of comets and, finally, in the meteorites which fall on the Earth.

It thus appears that the simplest organic compounds arise on the most diverse objects of the Universe without being dependent on life (abiogenically). It is hardly likely that our planet is an absolute exception to this general rule and that on it organic substances could never have been formed primarily. Would it not be more reasonable to suppose that this process took place on the Earth too at some earlier period of its history when it was still lifeless, and that it was only later that it was overshadowed by the more rapid and extensive biogenic synthesis?

The evidence of cosmogony and especially that from direct geological investigations fully justify such a supposition.

In his interesting book *The planets, their origin and development* H. Urey gave a profound analysis of the chemical processes which must have taken place when the Earth was formed and in the earliest stages of its existence. According to Urey the early chemical history of the Earth, like that of the other planets, was determined by the following underlying facts: 1, the distribution of the elements in the cosmos, especially in the cloud of dust and gas from which the solar system was formed; 2, the temperature prevailing at the various periods of the formation of the Earth; 3, the gravitational fields of the planets being formed; 4, the properties of the chemical substances of which they were being formed.

We may deduce the original composition of the protostar from which our solar system was formed from a study of the clouds of dust and gas which exist at present; in these the gas consists mainly of hydrogen which seems to be the predominant element in the cosmos generally (about 90 per cent. of the total mass). Helium and other inert gases are also present in these aggregates of dust and gas, but in much smaller amounts. The rest of the elements such as carbon, nitrogen, oxygen, iron, calcium, silicon etc. only constitute thousandths or tenthousandths of 1 per cent. of the total mass of the aggregation or even less than that.

The only substances which could exist in a gaseous form at the very low temperatures, near to absolute zero, which then prevailed are hydrogen, the inert gases and a compound of carbon and hydrogen which is widely distributed in the aggregates of dust and gas, namely methane. Compounds of other elements are present in the aggregates in the solid state in the form of particles of dust made up of metals and their oxides, water (in the form of ice or hydrates), silicates, compounds of sulphur and nitrogen etc.

After the Sun had become a self-luminous star and the discoidal protoplanetary cloud had been formed, different zones of it were at different temperatures. Owing to the radiation from the Sun the temperatures at various distances from it were approximately the same then as they are now.

Such free gases as hydrogen, helium and neon could not,

therefore, be retained in the zone in which the Earth was formed, owing to its relative proximity to the Sun. A considerable proportion of these was lost by the Earth during its formation. This is also true of the methane which was present in the original cloud of dust and gas. By far the greater part of this must have disappeared from the sphere of formation of the Earth and accumulated in colder parts of the protoplanetary cloud, settling on the surfaces of the large planets which were being formed there where, in fact, we do find an enormous amount of this hydrocarbon. All the non-volatile substances of the primary protoplanetary cloud, on the other hand, must, for the most part, have remained to make up the planetesimals which were formed in the region of the Earth. This also explains the fact that, so far as the heavy elements are concerned, the composition of the Earth is very like that of the Sun. The amounts of hydrogen, helium and other inert gases, on the contrary, are far less on Earth than in the Sun, notwithstanding the fact that the Sun and the Earth developed from the same original material as one another.

It is now very widely held that our planet was formed at a comparatively low temperature by the accumulation of cold solid bodies which differed in their composition, containing varying amounts of iron and silicates, but all lacking chemically inert and volatile compounds. In general, the chemical composition of these bodies must have been very like the average composition of contemporary meteorites.

The differences in composition and density between the solid substances from which the Earth was formed accounted for the heterogeneity of the interior which manifested itself during the later development of the Earth. This development was generally associated with gradual, localised heating of the surface of the planet, mainly due to the breakdown of radioactive elements within the Earth.

When this heating up had continued for a certain number of years and the interior temperature had reached 1000° C. or more, the solid formations became partly liquefied. Owing to the high pressure inside the Earth there was then a redistribution of substances, the heavier materials, rich in iron, sinking towards the centre while the lighter silicates rose to the surface. The crust of the Earth, or lithosphere, was thus formed on the

surface of the globe by the ' melting out ' of the more easily
melted compounds from the superficial layers of the Earth.
This process has been going on throughout all the geological
periods and cannot be considered as complete yet.

To-day the crust of the Earth consists of an envelope of
basalt and granite overlaid by a cover of sedimentary formations.   Underlying the crust there lies the so-called mantle
which is composed of ultra-basic material rich in silicon
(dunites).   The granitic envelope covers about a half of the
surface of the Earth, reaching its greatest thickness under the
continents and being absent from the bottom of the Pacific
Ocean.   The basaltic envelope, which lies beneath it, covers
the whole of the globe but it, too, is thinner under the oceans.

On the basis of his work on the zone melting of chondrites
or stony meteorites, A. Vinogradov convinced himself that the
dunites of the mantle are the residue from the ' melting out '
of the original material of the Earth which was similar in
composition to chondrites.   The ' melting out ' of the light
basaltic formations from the mass of the mantle under the
influence of radiogenic heat must have been accompanied by
the giving off of various vapours and gases either because they
were caused to become gaseous by the rise in temperature or
because they were formed by radioactive, radiochemical or
chemical processes going on in the solid envelopes of the
Earth.

THE EVOLUTION OF THE ATMOSPHERE AND HYDROSPHERE

The formation of the watery and gaseous envelopes of the
Earth (the hydrosphere and atmosphere) was thus very closely
associated, from the very beginning, with processes taking
place in the lithosphere.

The amount of water on the surface of the Earth at the
time under consideration must have been much less than it is
now.   Urey thinks that there was only about one tenth as
much water on the primitive Earth as there is in the seas and
oceans at present.   The rest of the water appeared later, being
liberated gradually from hydrated silicates as the lithosphere
was formed or, in general, from the combined constitutional
water of the interior of the Earth.

Although the Earth lost most of the hydrogen of its zone of

the protoplanetary cloud during its formation, the abundance of hydrogen in the material from which the Earth was originally formed had a considerable effect on the composition of the planet, especially its atmosphere. Even after the Earth had lost much of its free hydrogen it must have retained a very large amount of the element in the form of various compounds. During the formation of the crust of the Earth many of these were given off to form the atmosphere, which thus became strongly reducing.

Our present atmosphere, on the contrary, is well known to be very rich in free oxygen and therefore definitely oxidising. The abundance of gaseous oxygen, however, can only have arisen more recently, after the appearance of life on the Earth. If there was any free oxygen in the atmosphere of the Earth in the first stages of its existence there was only a very little.

Free oxygen could have been formed abiogenically in the crust of the Earth as a result of radiochemical reactions, in particular by the decomposition of the water of rock formations by α-rays. However, owing to its great activity, free oxygen would, during its passage through the mass of the crust of the Earth, oxidise the various unoxidised substances which are present there and could only reach the surface of the Earth in insignificant amounts. The gas liberated into the atmosphere as a result of the radio-decomposition of water in the rock formations therefore enriched the atmosphere with hydrogen rather than with oxygen. Free oxygen could also have been formed abiogenically in the outer layers of the atmosphere by the photochemical breakdown of water vapour by short-wave ultraviolet light. The gaseous hydrogen thus produced would have escaped into interplanetary space as it could not be held by the Earth's gravitational force, while the free oxygen would have remained in the atmosphere. Its concentration there, however, can never have been at all considerable as the waters of the ocean must have swallowed it up quickly. In them it oxidised the freely soluble reduced salts of iron to form the oxidised salts which precipitated out and sank to the bottom, gradually forming the enormous deposits of very ancient iron ores.

Nowadays there can be no doubt that the overwhelming mass of the free oxygen in the atmosphere as we know it has been formed biogenically, by photosynthesis, since the origin of life on the Earth. Even now, however, when the amount of free oxygen in the atmosphere is constantly being replenished by green plants, it is only the outermost skin of the crust of the Earth that is fully oxidised. The deeper layers are still in a highly reduced state in which they will combine very readily with oxygen. This may be seen from the commonly observed fact that volcanic lava and basalt are black, green or grey, indicating that these formations contain iron in an incompletely oxidised form, while sedimentary formations, such as clays and sands, are red or yellow because the iron in them is completely oxidised.

Thus we can see with our own eyes how atmospheric oxygen is gradually taken up as the igneous rocks are converted to sedimentary formations and it is only the continual process of photosynthesis which is now going on which ensures the replacement of this gas in the atmosphere of the Earth. According to the calculations of V. Goldschmidt, if all the vegetation on the surface of the Earth were now to be suddenly destroyed the free oxygen of the atmosphere would disappear in a few thousands of years, which is a very short time, geologically speaking. It would be taken up by the rock formations which are not fully oxidised.

The other important gas in the atmosphere at present is nitrogen. It must have been present at first on the surface of the Earth in its reduced form of ammonia, which is a compound of nitrogen and hydrogen. We have every reason to suppose that, in the solid material from which the Earth was formed, nitrogen was mainly present in the form of its compounds with metals, as metallic nitrides, or else as ammonium compounds. The presence of nitrides in the crust of the Earth is confirmed by the fact that geologists have found them there; they are also found in the lava thrown out by volcanoes. During the formation of the crust of the Earth nitrides must have reacted with the constitutional water of the interior of the Earth and the ammonia thus formed was given off from the surface of the Earth into the atmosphere. Geologists also find ammonium salts in the lithosphere. In volcanic gases and in those given off by geysers one may find considerable amounts of ammonia which have certainly been formed abiogenically.

Figures 2-6, 8, 9, 12, 15-17

Fig. 2. Star cluster of the Pleiades surrounded by a cloud of dust.

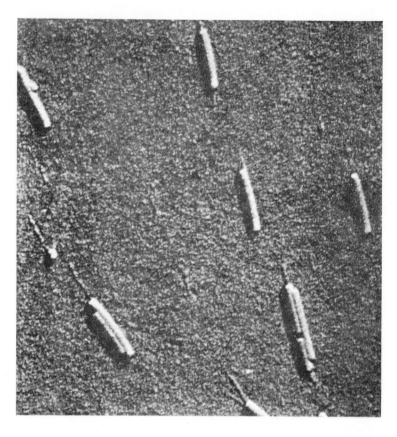

FIG. 3. Virus particles from which the protein has been removed in some places (after Hart).

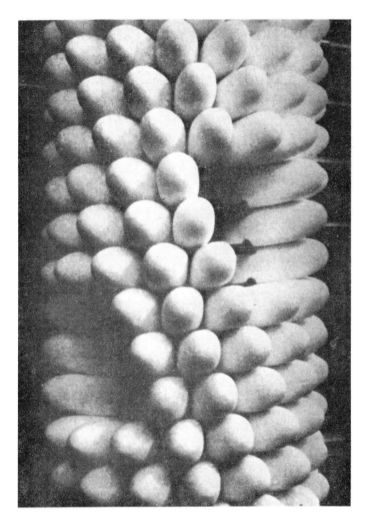

FIG. 4. Structural scale model of a particle of tobacco mosaic virus. Individual protein sub-units have been taken out of the model to show the single-stranded chain of RNA within the virus. The black structure represents RNA, the white protein.

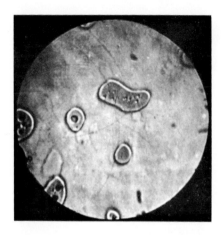

FIG. 5. Coacervates of serum albumin and
gum arabic.

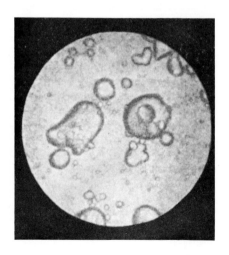

FIG. 6. Coacervate with three components:
gelatin, gum arabic and RNA.

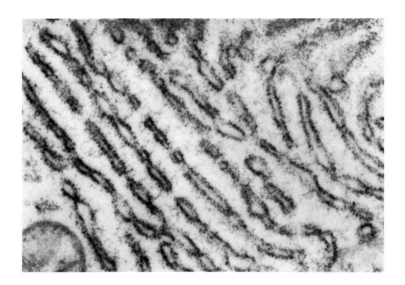

FIG. 8. Endoplasmic reticulum ×45,000 (after Palade).

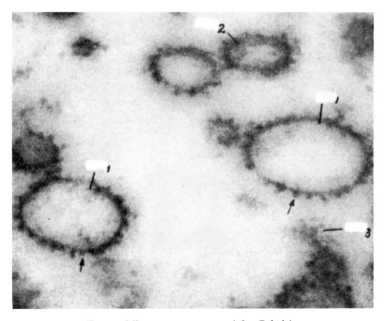

FIG. 9. Microsomes ×150,000 (after Palade).

1, median section; 2, medial section; 3, lateral section. Arrows indicate granules having diameters ∼ 150Å.

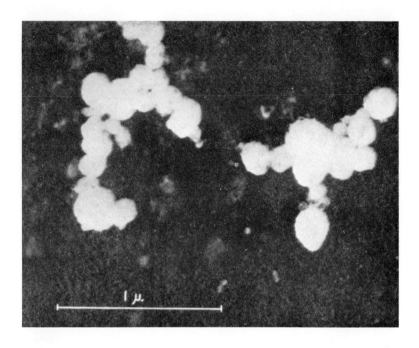

Fig. 12. Granules obtained from chloroplasts.

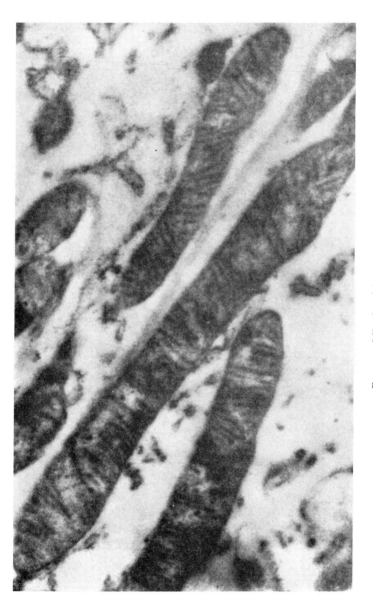

FIG. 15. Mitochondria ×41,000.

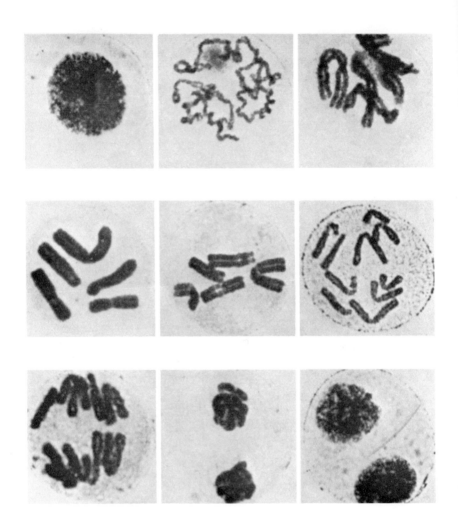

FIG. 16. Stages of mitosis in a plant, *Trillium*.

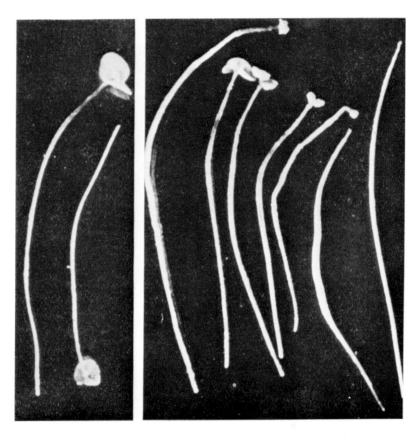

Fig. 17. Regeneration of fragments of *Acetabularia* containing no nuclei (after Brachet).

The free molecular nitrogen of our atmosphere has undoubtedly arisen secondarily by the oxidation of ammonia. V. Vernadskiĭ has also shown that an appreciable amount of the free nitrogen of the atmosphere could have been formed biogenically as a result of the vital activities of organisms.

Like nitrides, metallic sulphides in the crust of the Earth served as sources of hydrogen sulphide, a strongly smelling gas in which hydrogen is combined with sulphur. This gas must also have been present in the original reducing atmosphere of the Earth.

THE FORMATION OF HYDROCARBONS AND THEIR NEAREST DERIVATIVES DURING THE ORIGIN AND EARLIEST EXISTENCE OF EARTH

For our purposes we are specially interested in the nature of the compounds in which carbon first appeared on the surface of the Earth as this element forms the basis of all organic compounds without exception.

As we have already shown, the primary hydrocarbon of the protoplanetary cloud, methane, must have been lost to the Earth by leaving the zone in which it was formed. Only a small part of it might, perhaps, have been retained by being included in various formations in the planetesimals. More stable forms in which carbon may have been retained in the solid bodies of which our planet was formed are compounds of carbon with metals (carbides), and graphite. We find these substances as components of meteorites which correspond in their chemical composition with that of the material which served for the formation of the Earth. It is interesting to note that naturally occurring carbides were actually first discovered in a mineral which is characteristic of meteorites, namely cohenite which is, chemically, a compound of carbon with iron, nickel and cobalt. It was only later that cohenites of terrestrial origin were found. They are some of the compounds which derive from the deepest layers of the crust of the Earth. During their formation cohenites must undoubtedly have interacted with the water of the interior of the Earth with the formation of methane and other hydrocarbons. These gradually accumulated in the atmosphere of the Earth for, when once our planet had been formed they were held in its gravitational field and could not escape into interplanetary space.

One may imagine other ways in which hydrocarbons could have come into being during the formation of the crust of the Earth. In particular, they could have been formed by the direct reduction of graphite by the free hydrogen liberated by the radiochemical splitting of water. Some authors point to the possibility that the primary methane of the proto-planetary discoid might have been entrapped in the rocks and later have been given off.

Thus the evidence of planetary cosmogony is in complete agreement with the results of contemporary geochemical studies and they lead us to the conclusion that, on the Earth, as on other heavenly bodies, there not only might have been but must have been abiogenic formation of hydrocarbons and their nearest derivatives which are the simplest organic substances. The only question now at issue is which of the possible methods of abiogenesis of hydrocarbons was most common at the time of the formation of the Earth and during the following period of its existence. There can be no doubt whatever now that such abiogenesis must have occurred. It is confirmed by many direct geological observations.

As we have already shown, the formation of the crust of the Earth, which began in the very earliest period of its existence, cannot be said to be finished even yet. One may therefore hope that, in the deepest layers of the lithosphere where reducing conditions prevail and where none of the processes characteristic of life are taking place, one will discover the process of primary, abiogenic hydrocarbon formation. That hope is, in fact, justified. The possibility that hydrocarbons might be formed abiogenically under modern conditions is indicated by the existence of a number of gas-bearing formations which have no direct connection with sedimentary deposits. Such, for example, are the gaseous hydrocarbons which are formed in the crystalline formations of Lake Huron in Canada or in the Ukhta field in the U.S.S.R. The emissions of gas which have recently been discovered in the Khibiny massif in the Kola peninsula are of special interest in this connection. Investigation shows that they contain methane and heavier hydrocarbons. Extremely detailed examination of the physico-chemical and geochemical circumstances definitely indicate that the gases were formed from magma.

The number of cases in which petroleum has been found in igneous or metamorphic rocks has become far greater recently but, as these finds are very rarely of industrial importance and the amount present is insignificant, geologists and petroleum workers have paid very little attention to them. Nevertheless, finds of this sort have been made in many lands and may be counted by hundreds. In particular, liquid and gaseous hydrocarbons in the form of smears and insignificant emissions have also been found in very deep bores in crevices in the crystalline and metamorphic formations of the fundament which they could hardly have reached from sedimentary formations.

Thus, although the petroleum which is derived from sedimentary formations shows clear traces of its biological origin, there is no reason at all, on the basis of the facts we now know, to deny that petroleum may still be being formed abiogenically, even though only on a limited scale.

Before the origin of life these processes constituted the only means of formation of primary organic compounds, but with the origin of life there arose new and far more effective means of synthesising organic compounds, especially photosynthesis which makes use of that inexhaustible source of energy, sunlight. As a result of this a considerable proportion of the carbon on the surface of the Earth was drawn into the biological process and the old abiogenic method of formation of hydrocarbons receded into the background so that now one can only, with difficulty, find faint traces of it. In principle, however, it could still happen and in the past it was the only way in which organic substances could be formed.

Thus, all the evidence at present at our disposal as to the way in which our planet was formed and as to the later processes which occurred on its surface, as well as direct geochemical and geological observations, convince us that, from the very earliest periods of the formation of our planet, long before the origin of life on it, methane and various other hydrocarbons were formed by purely chemical, abiogenic means and accumulated on the surface of the Earth, in its crust, its hydrosphere and its atmosphere.

THE FURTHER DEVELOPMENT OF ORGANIC SUBSTANCES

Organic chemistry is regarded nowadays as being the chemistry of the hydrocarbons and their derivatives because these compounds have astonishing and unique chemical possibilities. No doubt, during the thousands of millions of years which elapsed between the formation of the Earth and the origin of life on it the hydrocarbons on its surface underwent many of these possible reactions. They could not remain unchanging for a long time but had to enter into chemical reactions both between themselves and with the other substances round them, forming a variety of complicated organic compounds quite unlike those of the inorganic world. This very fact gave them a special position in regard to the origin of life. Life could only arise on the Earth in the course of a process of regular increase in the complexity of organic compounds; without them there could be no life, although we can theoretically imagine other very complicated forms of organisation and motion of matter which would have had to develop on quite a different basis and in other ways from life. However, such bold (and generally ill-founded) fantasies are far from our field of interest as indicated in the first chapter.

How is it possible to trace out the chemical evolution of organic substances which was followed during those thousands of millions of years before the Earth was inhabited by living things?

At first glance it might seem that the simplest and most hopeful approach to the question would be by chemical work, aimed at finding and studying cases of the abiogenic transformation of carbon compounds going on at the present time under natural conditions and in the absence of life, just as we studied the formation of hydrocarbons in the process of formation of the crust of the Earth.

Such studies would, of course, give us much valuable information, but one must bear in mind the fact that life, having arisen at some time, has radically changed many of conditions prevailing on the surface of the Earth. It is now impossible to observe directly many of the phenomena which used to occur on the surface of the Earth in the past while, on the other hand, new processes are to be found there which were absent when the Earth was lifeless.

We have, therefore, no right to transfer contemporary geochemical findings mechanically to the remote epoch of the beginnings of our planet. We should correct these findings to a considerable degree, making extensive use of laboratory experimentation and trying to reproduce artificially the phenomena which once occurred on the surface of the lifeless Earth, meanwhile studying those transformations which the organic substances would undergo under these conditions.

Only a small amount of the hydrocarbons produced abiogenically in the lithosphere could have been retained for a long time in the original formations. All the volatile carbon compounds must gradually have been given off from the crust of the Earth into the atmosphere, as can still be seen in the case of natural fuel gases.

As we have shown earlier, before the origin of life the atmosphere of the Earth was fundamentally different from what it is now, in that it was reducing in nature. Only a very small proportion of the hydrocarbons given off into the atmosphere could, therefore, be oxidized directly by molecular oxygen to form carbon monoxide or even carbonic acid. However, even if it was formed, carbonic acid could not accumulate in any considerable amount in the primaeval atmosphere of the Earth for it would be deposited on the crust of the Earth in the form of carbonates after having reacted with the silicates of the lithosphere, and deposits of this substance would have appeared long before the origin of life. It was, however, after this event that the formation of carbonates took place especially intensively and now huge deposits of carbonate rocks serve as the sources from which the atmospheric carbon dioxide is replenished in the course of all sorts of volcanic phenomena.

The bulk of the hydrocarbons given off from the lithosphere reacted on the surface of the Earth with water vapour, ammonia, hydrogen sulphide and the other gases of its reducing atmosphere. This interaction was much facilitated by the short-wave ultraviolet radiation of the Sun which, at that time, could penetrate deeply into the atmosphere as it then was. The surface of the Earth is now shielded from the effects of these radiations by the so-called ' ozone screen '. At about 30 km. up in our present atmosphere there is a layer of ozone which has developed from molecular oxygen by the action of ultra-violet light on it. This layer absorbs all the short-wave part of the ultraviolet light. Obviously, with a reducing atmosphere and in the absence of molecular oxygen, there was no ozone screen and this created favourable conditions in the primaeval atmosphere for the various photochemical reactions to which the hydrocarbons were susceptible.

A second important source of energy for the abiogenic, organic-chemical transformation may have been the silent and sparking electric discharges which took place in the past and continue to do so in the atmosphere now (mainly in the form of lightning).

A very large amount of work has been published of recent years in the scientific literature in which attempts have been made to reproduce in the laboratory those conditions which must have prevailed in the primaeval atmosphere and the organic chemical reactions which occurred under those conditions.

In this way it has been shown that, under the influence of ultraviolet light or silent discharges, even such a com-paratively inert gas as methane can serve as the source of material for the formation of numerous organic compounds including oxygen, nitrogen, sulphur and phosphorus deriva-tives which may be aliphatic, aromatic or heterocyclic.

THE ORIGIN OF AMINO ACIDS

As an illustration we may cite the widely known experiments of S. Miller who caused silent discharges to pass through a gaseous mixture of methane, ammonia, hydrogen and water vapour and thus obtained amino acids, which are the most important components of the protein molecule. Similar syntheses of amino acids have been carried out by T. Pavlov-skaya and A. Pasynskiĭ using short-wave ultraviolet radiation.

These latter syntheses seem to us to be of particular interest owing to some special circumstances which we must examine more closely. At a certain stage in the course of the gradual increase in complexity of organic substances they acquired a new property which had not existed previously, namely dissymmetry. For example, methane and its simplest derivatives, methanol, formaldehyde and methylamine do not possess this property. It is even absent from glycine, the simplest amino acid. However, all the other, more complicated amino acids do possess this property.

THE ASYMMETRY OF ORGANIC SUBSTANCES

It may be explained as follows:—all dissymmetric organic compounds exist in two forms which are very like one another. Their molecules contain just the same atoms and groups of atoms but these groups are differently placed in space. If a particular radical is placed on the right in one form it will be placed on the left in the other and *vice versa*.

Our two hands can serve as a simple model of dissymmetric molecules. If we place them before us with the palms down we shall see that, for all their similarity, the right and left hand differ from one another in the arrangement of their different parts. If the thumb of the right hand is on the left the thumb of the left hand will be on the right. Thus each hand is, as it were, a mirror image of the other.

In ordinary, artificial syntheses of organic substances in our laboratories we always obtain an equal mixture of both forms of a dissymmetric molecule (called a racemic mixture). This is perfectly understandable, as the formation of one form or the other—the right or left antipode—depends on which of two atoms situated to the right or left of the plane of symmetry is exchanged for a new atomic group. However, the very concept of symmetry implies that both these atoms are subject to identical forces. The probability of the formation of one antipode or the other is therefore the same. As the law of averages applies to chemical reactions the appearance of an excess of one antipode is very improbable and, in fact, we never encounter it under the conditions of non-living nature and in laboratory syntheses. In Miller's syntheses, for example, the amino acids obtained were always racemic.

In living organisms, on the contrary, the amino acids of which naturally occurring proteins are made always have the left-handed configuration. In general, if an organism synthesises a dissymetric molecule it will almost always synthesise only one form. This ability of protoplasm selectively to synthesise and accumulate one antipode alone is called the asymmetry of living material. It is a characteristic feature of all organisms without exception but is absent from inanimate nature.

Pasteur pointed out this fact as follows:—" This great character is, perhaps, the only sharp dividing line which we can draw at present between the chemistry of dead and living nature." As early as the beginning of the 20th century it was shown that asymmetric syntheses are brought about in living things simply owing to the presence in them of previously existing asymmetry. The question naturally arose as to how the asymmetry had first occurred and, in general, whether it could have existed before the origin of life. F. Japp published an article called *Stereochemistry and vitalism* which caused a great stir at the time. In it he categorically denied that there was any possibility of primary asymmetric synthesis occurring outside living things. In his view asymmetry is a result of the action of a ' vital force ' and an asymmetric substance can, like a living thing, only arise out of another like it.

However, this idea was later refuted experimentally. The first asymmetric synthesis under laboratory conditions was, in fact, carried out by the use of photochemical reactions brought about by circularly polarised ultraviolet light. This suggests that in syntheses like those carried out by T. Pavlovskaya and A. Pasynskiĭ one might produce the asymmetric amino acids which are characteristic of living things if one used circularly polarised ultraviolet light. It has been shown that light of this sort did, in fact, exist under natural conditions on the Earth before life had arisen and therefore that asymmetric amino acids could have arisen there.

We now know of other ways in which asymmetric substances could have arisen primarily in the non-living world. For example, J. D. Bernal has recently suggested that the asymmetry of organic substances might have arisen on the surface of the Earth before the origin of life because the synthesis of these substances took place on the surfaces of asymmetric (left-handed or right-handed) crystals of quartz. This has been confirmed experimentally by A. Terent'ev and E. Klabunovskiĭ. Thus, if at the beginning of the century the so-called ' impossibility ' of the primary asymmetric synthesis of organic substances presented an insuperable obstacle to the development of life, that barrier has now been surmounted. In inorganic nature we meet with many factors which might account for the development of the asymmetric organic substances characteristic of living things even before the appearance of life on the planet. Even when we know how the asymmetry arose, though, we still cannot answer the question of why one antipode, rather than the other, should occupy such a monopolistic position in the life of all the organisms inhabiting the Earth. This question is important for an understanding of the essential nature of life but it remains for future investigators to supply the answer.

As the various organic substances which were formed in the atmosphere of the Earth became more complicated they lost their gaseous character and, to a greater and greater extent, they left the atmosphere for the primitive hydrosphere. The great mass of the organic compounds must have accumulated in the primaeval seas and oceans and this was the site of the fundamental process of formation of high-molecular substances and their transformation into the multimolecular systems from which life was derived.

The waters of the Earth at present contain a small amount of organic substances which have mostly come into being secondarily, as products of the vital activities of organisms or through the decay of their bodies.

Unfortunately, however, the waters of our present seas and oceans cannot serve as places where one may observe and study a process of gradual increase in complexity of organic substances under natural conditions similar to those which once led to the origin of life. This is due, in the first place, to their high content of free oxygen and, in the second, to the ubiquitous presence in them of living organisms.

According to the recent studies of the Soviet expeditionary ship *Vityaz* even the waters of the deepest parts of the ocean contain considerable amounts of oxygen. Only in a few exceptional cases as, for example, in the Norwegian fjords, can one get reducing conditions. But here too, like everywhere else, the waters are rich in organisms, especially anaerobic micro-organisms and, in the presence of organisms we are in no position to study the way in which abiogenic processes could have happened in the primitive hydrosphere. In this connection organisms confuse the issue. They give out into the external inorganic surroundings specific biogenic substances which could only be formed in the course of highly organised metabolism while, on the other hand, they take in other substances as food, involving them in their metabolism and using them to build their bodies.

We know now that Darwin wrote in a letter:—" It is often said that all the conditions for the first production of a living organism are present, which could ever have been present. But if (and oh! what a big if!) we could conceive in some warm little pond, with all sorts of ammonia and phosphoric salts, light, heat, electricity, etc., present, that a protein compound was chemically formed ready to undergo still more complex changes, at the present day such matter would be instantly devoured or absorbed, which would not have been the case before living creatures were formed."

It is therefore not so paradoxical as it might seem at first glance to say that the main reason why life cannot arise now under natural conditions is that it has already arisen.

The evolution of organic substances which preceded the origin of life could only have occurred under sterile conditions, that is, in the absence of organisms. Any organic material which might now be formed in one way or another under natural conditions would be destroyed quite quickly, being eaten by those creatures, so well equipped for the struggle for life, which inhabit every part of the earth, air and water.

The concentration of organic substances dissolved in sea water is now, therefore, very small and the possible duration of their evolution outside a living body is quite insignificant. On the surface of a world without life, on the other hand, there was nothing to prevent organic substances from evolving abiogenically over an unlimited period of time and accumulating in the waters of the primaeval seas and oceans in very considerable amounts.

If only half of the carbon which now exists on the surface of the Earth were to have existed then in the form of soluble organic substances, then their concentration in the waters of the primaeval ocean would have been at least some tenths of 1 per cent. This is calculated on the basis of all the waters then existing, but, of course, in some individual parts of it, some small enclosed basins, bays or lagoons, evaporation of water might lead to far higher concentrations. Furthermore, a local increase in the concentration of organic substances might have been achieved by their adsorption on clays or other inorganic sediments at the bottom or round the edge of the water as has already been suggested by J. D. Bernal. These deposits, and even the various dissolved inorganic salts, might also serve as very effective catalysts in carrying out a multitude of chemical transformations of organic substances.

THE ORIGIN OF PROTEIN-LIKE SUBSTANCES AND OTHER COMPLEX POLYMERS

A large volume of information has recently been accumulating in the scientific literature about many experimental results showing that, under the conditions we have described, processes of gradual polymerisation and condensation of various organic substances must have occurred extensively. Here we must refer, in particular, to the work of the Japanese scientist S. Akabori on his primary synthesis of 'fore-proteins' and to the similar studies of other authors communicated to the Moscow Symposium on the origin of life in 1957. From this work it follows that, at a particular period in the history of the Earth there must have developed in the waters of its hydrosphere numerous protein-like polymers of amino acids, polymers of nucleotides, polyglycosides and other complicated organic compounds of high molecular weight.

When they were formed primarily it was by an entirely different process from that which takes place now in the biosynthesis of proteins, nucleic acids and other organic polymers in the living cell. In protoplasm such syntheses are based on a very efficient organisation which is found in life alone and of which there could be no question in a simple solution of organic substances.

Thus, for example, the biosynthesis of a protein requires the co-ordinated participation of a series of protoplasmic systems:—

1. The system which furnishes the energy needed for the synthesis.

2. Enzymic systems controlling the relationships between the rates of the individual reactions, and

3. Systems determining the spatial configuration of the protein molecule. Nucleic acids, with their orderly structure, play the decisive part in this process.

It is only as a result of the co-ordinated actions of all these factors in the living cell that there can arise, not merely high-molecular polymers of amino acids, but the actual proteins which we can now isolate from objects of animal and vegetable origin. These have both a strictly determinate arrangement of amino acid residues in their polypeptide chains and a completely determinate intra-molecular folding of the chain to give a definite architecture to the protein globule as a whole. The biological peculiarities of each protein, its enzymic, hormonal, immunological or other functions in the living cell, are closely associated with the precise spatial relationships within the globule. Sometimes only a very small change in the configuration of the globule, or the sequence of amino acid residues in the polypeptide chain, is enough to cause the loss of all these properties by the protein affected. Thus, as living things have a form of organisation specific to themselves, proteins are constructed in them which are very well and effectively adapted to carrying out particular vitally important functions.

Similarly, the biosynthesis of nucleic acids having exactly the right structure requires the co-ordinated activity of systems peculiar to living things, among them some containing protein-enzymes with determinate structures.

It is quite clear that, in the solution of organic substances which constituted the waters of the primitive ocean before life had arisen, such biological laws governing biosynthetic processes could not have operated.

Here there was nothing of the strictly determined sequence of individual chemical transformations characteristic of biological metabolism, in which any original or intermediate compound chooses just one path from the many chemical possibilities open to it and then follows it steadily. A simple solution of organic substances is quite different. In it all possible chemical transformations cut across one another

*Figures 3 and 4 follow page 52.

repeatedly, becoming twisted up in a complicated tangle of interactions. The polymers formed in such a solution therefore lacked the regularity and internal adaptation to their particular biological function which are so characteristic of contemporary proteins and nucleic acids. The laws of thermodynamics and chemical kinetics, which alone determined the course of chemical events on the still lifeless Earth, are enough to give us a rational explanation as to why there must have arisen, in the waters of the primaeval ocean, only a variety of poly-peptides, polynucleotides and other polymers having a rather disorderly distribution of links in their molecules i.e. compounds which did not have an internal structure comparable to that of contemporary proteins and nucleic acids, the 'purposive-ness' of whose structure was determined by biological laws which came into existence later.

Could it then be that, among the endless multitudes of possible variants, there could have arisen, perhaps only once in the whole time of the existence of the Earth, a molecule of nucleic acid or nucleoprotein having an internal structure which enabled it to reproduce itself? Such a molecule would then begin to 'multiply' without limits in the 'primaeval broth' of the hydrosphere and life would have begun.

This concept of the origin of life even at the unimolecular level of evolution of organic substances is very alluring on account of its apparent simplicity and it is therefore fairly widely recognised in modern scientific literature.

Its popularity increased, particularly in connection with the development of the study of filterable viruses. These cause a number of diseases in man, animals and plants and it is now known that, comparatively speaking, they have a very simple chemical nature. This applies particularly to the virus of tobacco mosaic, which was obtained in crystalline form by W. Stanley as early as 1935. The crystals seemed to be an individual chemical substance as far as their composition was concerned. It is a compound of a nucleic acid with a protein, a nucleoprotein with a specific structure. If this substance is introduced into a living cell of a tobacco plant there will be, in that plant, a very rapid process of biosynthesis of the same protein and nucleic acid which are characteristic of the virus but which were absent from the original healthy

leaf of the tobacco plant. There is, as one might say, ' multiplication ' of the molecules of viral nucleoprotein.

The hypothesis is usually put forward that, purely by
chance, there developed in ' the primaeval broth ' a molecule
like that of the nucleic acid of the tobacco mosaic virus which
began to multiply there and thus constituted the ' first living
molecule ', the beginning of life on the Earth.

It is, however, a fact that viruses cannot multiply in such
a ' broth ' or in any artificial medium, though the number of
media tried is extremely large. The increase in the amount of
virus only occurs in a living cell and this does not seem to be
a matter of chance but is inherent in the actual nature of the
process involved.

The cell of the tobacco plant before the introduction of the
virus is already synthesising its own nucleoproteins on the
basis of the interaction of the energetic, catalytic and structural
systems in the protoplasm which we have already mentioned.
The incorporation of the specific viral nucleoprotein, (or even
of just its nucleic acid) makes some change in the relationships
of the enzymic and other processes, it distorts the final link in
the biosynthetic process in such a way that, instead of leading
to the production of the plant's own nucleic acid which plays
a part in its metabolism, it leads to the production of viral
nucleoprotein which is foreign to the plant and accumulates
in it in very large amounts.

Thus this is not ' multiplication ' of the virus in the biological sense, not its self-reproduction on some nutrient
medium. All that takes place is the constant new formation of
a specific nucleoprotein with the help of the biological systems
of the tobacco leaf. This means that the new formation is only
possible in the presence of an organisation which is peculiar
to life and consequently the first living thing was not a virus;
on the contrary, viruses, like other modern specific proteins
and nucleic acids, could only have arisen as products of the
biological form of organisation.

Even if there had developed by chance in the ' primaeval
broth ' a molecule with the specific structure of a viral
nucleoprotein (which is, in itself, very unlikely), even then
' multiplication ', ' self-reproduction ' or constantly repeated
new formation of such a molecule could not have happened

there as it would have required the strictly organised co-ordination of complicated systems including, in particular, a whole series of specifically constructed protein-enzymes which, in their turn, could only have arisen as a result of biological organisation.

As we have already shown, the presence of proteins is needed for the ordered biosynthesis of nucleic acids while the biosynthesis of proteins necessarily requires the participation of nucleic acids. One therefore often hears the question:— In the process of the origin of life, which were formed first, proteins or nucleic acids? This question is as academic as the old problem of the hen and the egg. Obviously every hen comes from an egg and every hen's egg from a hen. It there-fore used to seem completely impossible to answer the question as to whether the hen or the egg came first. It is, however, only the metaphysical approach which leads to such a conclusion by trying to solve the problem in complete isolation from the history of the development of living matter. If we turn to this history we shall see that both the hen and its egg arose at some stage of evolutionary development as a result of successive increases in complexity and efficiency of more primitive living things which were less well adapted to the conditions of their existence.

It is as unjustifiable to discuss the possibility that specific proteins or nucleic acids with orderly structures might have been formed primarily in the waters of the primaeval ocean. The only substances of this sort which could have arisen there are polymers with an incomparably simpler organisation and, of course, completely lacking any biological function. Only considerably later and at a far higher level of the evolutionary process, did it become possible for either proteins or nucleic acids of the modern type to develop.

It is a characteristic feature of life that it is not distributed through space but manifests itself in individual, very com-plicated systems which are delimited from the external world, namely organisms. These organisms continually interact with their environment and have an internal structure which is extremely well adapted for ensuring their prolonged survival, continual self-renewal and self-reproduction under the conditions prevailing in the external world.

THE FORMATION OF COACERVATES

A form of organisation and motion of matter of this kind could only have arisen by the separating out of complete multimolecular systems from the homogeneous solution of organic substances which is sometimes referred to as the ' primaeval broth '. At first, maybe, these systems were very primitive but already able to interact with the external medium by virtue of their own demarcation from that medium. This very process of interaction and the associated selection of individual primary systems for length of persistence under given external conditions formed the basis for the gradual adaptation of the internal organisation of these systems to suit the external conditions and for the occurrence of more and more effective interactions with the environment involving substances and processes. This led to the development of the organised metabolism which lies behind the formation of the proteins, nucleic acids and other ' purposively ' constructed and functionally adapted substances which characterise the modern organism.

It would, of course, be very difficult to decide what determined the process of formation of the primary systems from which organisms arose. It may be held that it was the separation of clots of organic substance by their adsorption on particles of clay or on other solid, inorganic particles as J. D. Bernal supposes. S. Fox has recently demonstrated the very interesting possibility of forming protein-like multimolecular systems by the action of heat on mixtures of amino acids under natural conditions. Not long ago R. Goldacre put forward an intriguing idea as to the formation of globules enclosed in envelopes of lipoprotein. He thinks that the individual globules might have arisen from the action of the wind in causing the collapse of films covering the surfaces of natural bodies of water.

One may picture to oneself many other ways in which the separation of the original multimolecular systems from the homogeneous solution of organic compounds of the hydrosphere might have happened. However, it seems to me most likely, for reasons which will be discussed later, that such systems first arose in the form of what are known as coacervate droplets.

*Figures 5 and 6 follow page 52.

Such droplets can easily be obtained under laboratory conditions by the simple mixing of solutions of different proteins and other substances of high molecular weight at ordinary temperatures and in most cases with very little acidity. In this way the molecules taking part in coacervate-formation, which were previously distributed evenly throughout the solvent, unite with one another at particular points in space to form whole molecular swarms or clumps which separate themselves out from the solution, when they reach a particular size, in the form of sharply demarcated droplets, which are visible under the microscope floating in the surrounding medium. This medium, known as the equilibrium liquid, is now almost devoid of the substances of high molecular weight which had previously been dissolved in it, these having all been concentrated in the coacervate droplets.

These formations have been studied for many years by the Dutch scientist Bungenberg de Jong and are now being investigated in many laboratories throughout the world. The classical substances for forming coacervates in Bungenberg de Jong's work were solutions of gelatin and gum arabic. One can, however, obtain coacervates of many rather than two components, by mixing together various proteins, for example, casein, egg or serum albumin, haemoglobin, pseudoglobulin, glycinin, clupeine etc. Furthermore, coacervates may also be formed with nucleic acids, various polyoses such as amylophosphoric acid or araban, lecithin and other lipids (in the form of lipoprotein complexes) and other such substances. The droplets may also contain active enzymes which continue to manifest their specific catalytic activities inside the droplet. Bungenberg de Jong believes that electrostatic and hydration forces play a fundamental part in the formation of coacervates. In view of the extreme complexity of the phenomenon, however, the theory of coacervation cannot be considered as fully worked out. The process of coacervation can also be treated in terms of substances which are soluble, to a limited extent, in one another separating out to give layers or droplets of two liquid phases. If however, the stability of the droplets in a coacervate of simple liquids is determined by the magnitude of the surface tension between the droplets and the medium in which they are suspended, then, in coacervates of proteins or other substances of high molecular weight, the conditions for stabilisation of the drops are far more complicated. This is determined, to a considerable extent, by the action of adsorption layers on the surface separating the droplets from the medium. This stabilising action is particularly marked when the layer in question has a high structural viscosity or even elasticity and mechanical resistance to deformation. If these conditions are met the stability of the droplet may be extremely great.

When coacervates of proteins or other such substances are formed there is a partial migration of molecules of proteins and their associated lipids or polysaccharides to the surface of separation of the droplet, where they form molecular layers with altered structures and mechanical properties. This accounts for the presence of a sharply defined surface, with rather rigid mechanical properties demarcating the droplets of complex coacervates from their equilibrium liquids.

Coacervate droplets of protein may also have an internal structure which is quite different from that found in simple droplets of liquid. This structure usually takes the form of a very labile orientation of the particles of the coacervate but, in some cases, this orientation may be fairly stable.

From our point of view so-called multiple complex coacervates are of special interest. These are made up of components of several different kinds, for example, a coacervate of gelatin, gum arabic and sodium nucleate. This can exist as a single coacervate or may form two immiscible coacervates. When this happens the large droplets of the one coacervate contain the smaller droplets of the other.

Associated with the presence of an internal structure and a definite organisation of the surface which separates the droplet from the equilibrium liquid, coacervates have a marked power of adsorbing various substances from the surrounding solution. Many organic substances are almost entirely removed from the equilibrium liquid by appropriate coacervates even when the concentration of the coacervates is no more than a thousandth part of 1 per cent. It is very important, in this connection, that such adsorption is selective. Coacervates may collect large amounts of one substance, drawing it out of the dilute solution around them, while, on the other hand, they may only take up a very limited amount of another substance, even when this is present in a higher concentration in the equilibrium mixture. It is now possible to formulate the reasons which have led me to believe that coacervate droplets are the most likely form of organisation of individual multimolecular systems to have formed the basis for further evolution. In the first place there was the primary formation in the waters of the primaeval ocean of various organic compounds of high molecular weight in the form of irregularly constructed polymers of carbohydrates, amino acids or nucleotides. From a colloid-chemical point of view these cannot have been very different from those which we find to-day. Solutions of these substances, like present-day solutions of proteins, polysaccharides and nucleic acids, have a very marked tendency towards the formation of intermolecular associations. As the formation of coacervate droplets does not require any special conditions for its occurrence but happens when solutions of various polymers are simply mixed together, it must have occurred as a direct consequence of the formation of these polymers in the primaeval ocean. In the second place, it would hardly be possible to find a means of concentrating protein-like substances and others of high molecular weight which would be nearly as effective as coacervation, especially at ordinary, relatively low temperatures. It is well known that one can obtain coacervation in solutions containing only one part of gelatin to 100,000 parts of water. As we have already shown, the concentration of organic substances in the primaeval ocean of the Earth must have been at least a hundred times as great as this.

In the third place, the coacervate droplets which separated out from the ' primaeval broth ' were not completely isolated from the medium surrounding them. They did not turn into closed systems but retained the possibility of interacting with the external medium, which was a prerequisite for their further development.

Fourth and finally, the phenomenon of coacervation is particularly interesting from our point of view because the material carrier of life in its present form—protoplasm—is also, from a physico-chemical point of view, a multiple, complex coacervate.

This, of course, does not mean that every coacervate droplet is, in some way, living. There is a profound difference between protoplasm and ordinary coacervates, based, in the first instance, on the fact that the stability of the two systems, which means their ability to exist for prolonged periods, is founded on completely different principles.

THEIR TRANSFORMATION INTO OPEN SYSTEMS

The coacervates which we make artificially and the droplets which arose naturally by separation from the organic solution of the waters of the ocean are, in themselves, static systems. The longer or shorter duration of their existence is associated with the maintenance of the constancy of the properties of the system in time. It depends on them being in a state of thermodynamic stability. The more unchanging a droplet, from the colloid-chemical point of view, the fewer its chances of disappearing as an individual formation in a particular stretch of time, either by coalescing with other droplets or by disintegrating into the surrounding solution.

In contrast, the coacervate structure characteristic of living protoplasm can only exist so long as it carries out, in uninterrupted and rapid succession, that multitude of bio-chemical processes which together constitute metabolism. If these processes cease or are substantially changed the proto-plasmic system itself is destroyed. Its prolonged existence and the constancy of its form are not associated with changelessness or rest, but with constant motion.

Analogous systems exist in the inorganic world; they have been given the general name of open, or flowing systems. The constancy of their properties in time is characterised, not by thermodynamic equilibrium (as in closed systems isolated from their environment), but by the existence of the stationary state in which there is maintained a certain constancy of processes flowing in one direction. This stationary state, which exists in open systems, is similar to the thermodynamic equilibrium of closed systems in that, in both cases, the systems concerned maintain the constancy of their properties in time. The essential difference between them is that in thermodynamic equilibrium there is no overall change in free energy ($dF = 0$) whereas in the stationary state it is changing all the time but at a constant rate (dF = const.).

The following elementary examples may be presented. An ordinary bucket of water may serve as a model of a closed, static system which maintains a constant water level owing to the absence of any processes. On the other hand, a tank of running water, in which the water flows in through one pipe and out through another, is a stationary open system. The level of the water in such a tank may be kept constant, but only by having a particular constant relationship between the rates of inflow and outflow. By changing the relationship we can achieve some other level which will then maintain its stationary state under the new conditions.

In this very simple example we have considered a system in which no chemical change was taking place, but for our purposes the more complicated chemical open systems are of greater interest. In systems of this sort there is also a constant accession of matter from the environment into the system, which is demarcated in some way from its surroundings, but in this case the substances undergo a chemical change and the products of the reaction are returned to their environment. The constancy of such a system in time is therefore that of the stationary state, in which there is not only a constant relationship between the rates of intake and output of substances, but also between them and the rates at which chemical changes take place within the system.

The simplest form of such a system may be represented by the following diagram:—

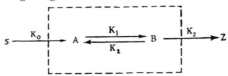

The dotted line indicates the boundary between the system and the environment, S and Z represent the environment itself, while A and B represent substances undergoing chemical change in the system. K_0 and K_z are constants representing the rate at which substances cross the boundary, by diffusion or otherwise, and K_1 and K_2 are the velocity constants of the reactions going on inside the system.

When the rates of diffusion and reaction remain constant the system reaches a stationary state with a definite ratio between the concentrations of its components. Any alteration of the parameters will entail an upset of the equilibrium but afterwards a new stationary state will be established. The number of such possible states is unlimited. Thus, if we include in such a system a catalyst which accelerates one reaction, there will be an adjustment of the relationships between all the components such as is quite impossible in a closed system, where the introduction of a catalyst only alters the rate at which equilibrium is attained and not its level.

In the living cell matters are incomparably more complicated than in this simple chemical diagram. In the first place, we have to consider, not one individual reaction, but a whole chain of strictly co-ordinated chemical transformations. The sugar which enters a yeast from the wort surrounding it is there transformed into the final products of the fermentation, namely alcohol and carbon dioxide. This does not happen directly, as the result of a single chemical act, but as the result of a complicated series of specific reactions which are integrated with one another. These are:—phosphorylation, isomerisation, reduction, breaking of carbon bonds etc.

By analogy with the previous diagram this may be represented as follows:—

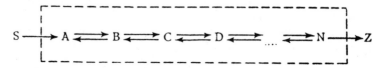

However, if the transformation of substances in a living cell just took the form of a simple, unbranched chain of chemical reactions, it would have no biological point. One might say that alcoholic fermentation according to the above scheme is taking its own course without being of any use to the yeast cell.

In fact things do not happen like that, but the chain branches in an orderly way at certain points. At the points where these branches occur there is a diversion of the energy-rich substances needed for the synthesis of ' structural material ' along collateral channels of co-ordinated reactions leading to the production of compounds which are of value for the construction of the living body.

Thus we may make our diagram even more complicated and present it as follows:—

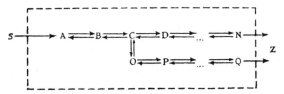

The products of these synthetic reactions may be given off into the external world as shown in the diagram or they may be retained for a longer or shorter time within the cell subserving its growth.

Finally, the chains of biochemical reactions may form closed cycles, as for example:—

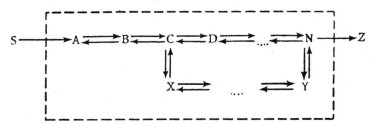

In these cycles there is a certain repetition of chemical processes. In the more remote offshoots of the chain, however, there is always an irreversible branching off of processes, so that biological metabolism as a whole always flows in the same direction.

In protoplasm there are numerous metabolic chains and cycles joined together into a single, much branched metabolic network with an orderly structure which C. Hinshelwood has compared to a well-developed railway network, on which many trains are running at the same time but at different speeds.

It is characteristic of the living body that the whole of this complicated and orderly sequence of phenomena is constantly directed towards the continued self-preservation and self-reproduction of the whole living system under the environmental conditions prevailing at a given time.

What are the immediate causes underlying this sequence? From all that has been said it is clear that the relationship between the rates at which different reactions take place in the living body plays a fundamental part. From this point of view the organic substances which form the material basis of protoplasm, are extremely suitable material for the construction of such a network as has been described above. It is a feature of organic substances, that they can react in the most diverse directions and, although they have an enormous variety of chemical possibilities, they realise these possibilities at a very slow rate under ordinary conditions and in the isolated state. However it is possible to act on them in such a way as to accelerate selectively just one of the possible reactions of a given compound and thus to force the compound to stick to a particular and strictly determinate direction in its chemical reactions and not to stray along all the paths open to it. The path followed is the one along which the reaction proceeds most quickly.

A simple solution or uniform mixture of organic substances presents itself, in this respect, as a very wide but completely untamed field of chemical possibilities; it is possible to move in any direction but always with the same great difficulty and therefore at the same slow rate. In contradistinction to this, protoplasm presents definite pathways of biochemical processes, a whole network of ' rationally constructed tracks ' along which chemical transformations, with their concomitant conversion of energy, continually proceed at a tremendous rate in ' strict conformity with the rules '. The co-ordination of the rates of the individual metabolic reactions which make up this complete series is regulated, in the living body, by a number of factors, the most important of which is the catalytic activity of enzymes.

Owing to the specificity of their structure, present-day protein-enzymes are extremely efficient chemical agents in protoplasm. With their help, not only are the biochemical reactions necessary for the rapid flow of the vital processes accelerated, but they are directed along particular tracks. This happens because enzymes are unlike the other catalysts of the inorganic world. In the first place they have an extremely powerful catalytic effect; in the second place they have a very great catalytic specificity; in the third place they are markedly labile so that the strength of their catalytic activity can vary within very wide limits under the influence of a great variety of external influences and internal factors.

This may be clarified by reference to the following simple scheme. Let us suppose that the organic substance A can be converted into substances B, C, D, etc. In the accompanying diagram these transformations are represented by radial vectors the lengths of which correspond with the rates of the respective reactions.

Thus the rate of the reaction $A \rightarrow B$ is seven times that of the reaction $A \rightarrow D$ while this reaction proceeds only half as fast as $A \rightarrow C$. Naturally, when a given time has passed and all the substance A which was originally present has disappeared, the resulting mixture will consist of 70 per cent. B, 20 per cent. C and 10 per cent. D. If we make some nonspecific alteration which accelerates all the reactions equally, the changes will proceed more quickly but the proportions of the products obtained at the end will remain the same. As before, substance B will predominate. If, however, we introduce into the original mixture an enzyme which will accelerate the reaction $A \rightarrow D$ by many millions of times without affecting the rates of the other reactions, almost all of substance A will be converted into substance D and the other possible reactions will have no practical significance.

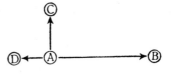

The substance D which has thus arisen, like any other organic compound, has many chemical potentialities, but, in the presence of a new specific enzyme, it will only follow the one path laid out for it by that enzyme. Thus there arises a chain of consecutive reactions co-ordinated with one another in time.

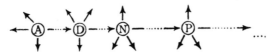

But such a chain is only possible where there is a whole series of enzymes each of which is specific for the corresponding link in the chain. And, in fact, in Buchner's juice, which is extracted from yeast, we may find a large collection of enzymes which, acting concurrently, can reproduce the chain of reactions by which sugar is converted into alcohol and carbon dioxide, though essentially in a one-track way, without any branching of the chain.

When we are dealing with a branched chain of reactions rather than with a simple one we must take into account, not only the presence of all the necessary enzymes, but also the relationship between their catalytic activities. In such a case the intermediate products formed at the points where the chain branches follow, not one, but at least two paths. The proportion following each path depends on the relative catalytic activity of the specific enzymes involved in these paths.

In the living body, with its extremely elaborate network of metabolism, the matter is even more involved. Here there must be a precise, yet very versatile, co-ordination of the catalytic activities of all the enzymes in the well-stocked arsenal of the protoplasm. This co-ordination is largely based on the high lability of enzymes, the great variability of their activity under the influence of many external and internal agents.

There is no physical or chemical factor, no organic compound or inorganic salt which cannot, in one way or another, affect the course of enzymic reactions. Any rise or fall of temperature, any change in the acidity of the medium, its oxido-reduction potential, the salts dissolved in it or its osmotic pressure, will interfere with the relationship between the rates of the enzymic reactions and thus alter their mutual connections in the network of metabolic reactions. In this respect the development within protoplasm of a new sort of specific activators or inhibitors, which selectively strengthen or weaken the activity of one or other of the protoplasmic enzymes, is very important.

We must also bear in mind the exceptional part played by the spatial organisation of protoplasm in biological metabolism. Enzymes are mainly concentrated on interfaces and on the structural formations of protoplasm. They are, as one might say, rationally 'assembled' here into 'production lines' each of which fulfils its own biological function. Any alteration in these lines may, not merely raise or lower the rate of the reactions catalysed by the enzymes, but may displace the stationary equilibrium of chemical reactions in the direction of synthesis or breakdown. This will naturally be of decisive importance for the stability of the whole living system, even for its survival under the given environmental conditions.

To summarise what has been said. The most important thing to notice is the extreme complexity and variety of the factors determining the organisation of modern protoplasm i.e. those on which the structure of the network of metabolic reactions depends. This whole phenomenon is based on the chemical properties of the organic compounds of which the living body is made up. The great variety of these compounds and their wide range of reactivity in themselves ensure the possibility of many chemical transformations and innumerable combinations of them. Through this extensive field of chemical possibilities, life has traced out definite paths of biochemical processes. It is a characteristic feature of living things that they have a very highly developed network of metabolic reactions, the organisation of which is determined by an elaborate complex of factors of different kinds, namely, the presence of a particular collection of enzymes, their quantitative relationships, the physical and chemical circumstances obtaining in the protoplasm, its colloidal properties and, finally, the structural or spatial organisation of its molecules and multimolecular systems.

The substances which play the leading parts in the organisation of living bodies are not those which enter them by chance, but the proteins, nucleic acids and other complicated and multifarious organic compounds which are constantly being formed in protoplasm and which have a specific structure associated with specific biological functions. The continued production of such compounds and the formation of structures from them is ensured by the efficiency of the organisation of the network of metabolic reactions. On the other hand, each of these substances and structures has some sort of influence on the rates, directions and interconnections of the reactions taking place in the protoplasm and, hence, on the regular sequence which gave rise to the particular composition of the protoplasm and its structures.

In this way there arises a circle of extremely close knit,

interpenetrating phenomena. We may understand each individual link in this circle in terms of physics and chemistry. In this way we may find out *how* any particular compounds or structures are formed in protoplasm and *how* they affect the rate and sequence of biochemical reactions in the whole metabolic network. However, the application of these laws alone in a physical and chemical study of living bodies in the form in which they exist to-day will never enable us to answer the question as to *why* this living series is what it is, so integrated and adapted to the continued self-preservation and self-reproduction of the living system as a whole under the given conditions of its existence. To do so we must consider the question in its evolutionary context, studying the successive improvements which ensured the transformation of the original, still lifeless systems into the first living things, which were already very highly organised. This can hardly have happened by chance but must have followed some law.

THE EVOLUTION OF THE ORIGINAL COACERVATE SYSTEMS

The coacervate droplets which were formed in the waters of the hydrosphere were an inevitable consequence of the formation there of polymers similar to proteins and nucleic acids. Their formation was, however, also a very important stage in the process of evolution of abiogenic organic substances. Before this organisation had occurred the organic material of the ' primaeval broth ' was inextricably mixed up with the surrounding medium and did not form an entity of its own. With the formation of coacervates the molecules of organic substances became concentrated at particular points in space and were separated from the surrounding medium by a more or less sharp boundary. In this way there arose complete multimolecular systems each of which already had a certain individuality and, in this sense, stood out against all the rest of the world around it. The later history of one such coacervate droplet might differ substantially from that of another individual system existing alongside it. The fate of the drop was, already, not determined solely by the general conditions of the external medium, but also by its own specific internal organisation in both space and time. In its details, this organisation was

peculiar to the individual and other droplets might have somewhat different arrangements, each of which was also peculiar
to an individual.

What conditions determined the individual existence of any
coacervate molecule in the waters of the primaeval hydrosphere? Complex coacervates obtained artificially by the
simple mixture of solutions of two colloidal complexes are,
as we have seen, formations with a static form of stability.
Their longer or shorter period of survival is determined by
their relative solubilities or the presence of a surface film which
conserves the constancy of the properties of the system in time.

This, however, was not the sort of stability for a system
which was to play the decisive part in the evolution of matter
along the road to the origin of life. This evolution could only
take place on the basis of interaction between the system and
the medium around it, that is to say, on the basis of the formation of open systems. The coacervate drops which, in one way
or another, were forming in the primaeval hydrosphere, were
not simply immersed in water but in a solution of various
organic compounds and inorganic salts.

These substances from the environment must have passed
selectively through the surface film of the drops or have been
adsorbed selectively by the compounds present in them, and
entered into some sort of reactions with these compounds,
the products being either retained in the droplet or passing
out of it again into the external medium. Of course, these
reactions occurred very slowly and did not form any inter-
connected network of processes; however, they were not, as
yet, prerequisites for the prolonged existence and stability of
the coacervate droplet. None the less, even at this primitive
stage of the evolution of our original systems these must have
had two properties which were very important for the further
development of matter.

On the one hand, the individual physico-chemical
peculiarities of organisation of particular coacervate droplets
impressed their own stamp on the chemical reactions which
went on inside them. The presence of this or that substance
or radical in a particular droplet, the presence or absence of the
simplest inorganic catalysts such as salts of iron, copper,
calcium etc., the degree of concentration of protein-like and

other substances of high molecular weight forming the coacervate, its particular structure—all this is implicit in the rates
and directions of various chemical reactions which had taken
place in the given drop. All this gave a specific character to
the chemical processes which developed in it. Thus, there
was a certain correlation between the structure and organisation
of a given droplet and the chemical transformations which
took place in it. In different droplets these transformations
were co-ordinated differently in time, depending on the
individual peculiarities of the given system.

SELECTION OF THE ORIGINAL SYSTEMS

On the other hand, any chemical processes, even if incomplete, occurring in any droplet, or, even more so, any
concatenation of such processes, did not necessarily always
suffer the same fate. One such might confer great stability
and a prolonged existence on a particular droplet under
particular external circumstances. From this point of view
it would be useful, it would have a positive significance.
Other such processes or concatenations, on the contrary,
would have a negative character, being harmful to the given
individual formation, leading to the disintegration and
disappearance of the systems in which they developed. However, such coacervate systems could not play any substantial
part in the further evolution of organic formations as their
individual history was of short duration and soon came to an
end. The only systems which had a more or less prolonged
existence under these circumstances were those having an
individual organisation which subserved a collection of
chemical reactions which were favourable to its existence.

Thus, even at this stage in the evolution of matter there
arose a certain selection of organised colloidal systems. The
systems selected were those in which the organisation was
suited to the task of maintaining the existence of the particular
organism under conditions in which it was continually interacting with the medium surrounding it.

Of course, this ' selection ' was still very primitive and
cannot be directly and fully equated with ' natural selection '
in the strictly biological sense of the term. However, the
further evolution of individual organic systems proceeded

under its auspices and therefore acquired a definite direction. First of all, as a result of this directional evolution, the very nature of the stability of the original colloidal systems was fundamentally changed.

The stability of the coacervate droplets which first developed in the waters of the primitive hydrosphere may originally have been based on the same static principles as that of the coacervates of gelatin and gum arabic which are obtained artificially in the laboratory. The coacervate state and the organisation of the processes which were being carried out in the droplet might, to a certain extent, have existed independently of one another. However, for the reasons given above, as evolution acquired a direction these two processes must have become more and more organised into a single unit because the existence of the system depended on the network of reactions being accomplished within it while, on the other hand, the network itself was determined by the organisation of the system as a whole. When there is constant interaction with the external medium in the absence of such co-ordination, the system must disintegrate very quickly and disappear as an individual formation. If the interaction between the system and the medium is broken off for any reason, the static system is automatically excluded from the general process of evolution.

For example, if the stability of coacervate droplets depended on the formation of firm surface membranes which disintegrated spontaneously at a particular rate but could be reconstructed in the course of chemical reactions within the droplet, the stability of the droplet would be determined by the relationship between the rates of the processes of disintegration and reconstruction of the surface layers. If the rate of formation of the firm surface layers were high, then the dynamic stability of the droplets might also be very high. In such a case acceleration of the chemical reactions within the droplet would ensure its stability and hence its 'survival' under given external conditions. This acceleration would act as a stabilising factor in the droplet. If the rate of formation of the surface layer were less than that of its destruction the droplets would soon break down. Finally, if the surface layers of the droplets themselves acquired great rigidity and extreme stability unconnected with any chemical reactions within the droplet, then such a static colloidal system would be excluded from the evolutionary process. Accordingly, as a result of the directed evolution of the original systems, their stability took on a more and more dynamic character. The coacervate droplets were gradually transformed into open systems the very existence of which, under particular environmental conditions, depended on the organisation of the processes being carried out within them. In other words, there arose systems which were capable of self-preservation by virtue of the constant processes of self-renewal going on in them. Their prolonged existence was, in fact, based on continual interaction with the external medium. This appearance of the power of self-preservation may be regarded as the first result of the directed evolution of our original systems.

The second step forward in the same direction was the emergence of systems capable, not only of self-preservation, but also of growth, of increasing their mass at the expense of material from the surrounding medium. The stationary state of open systems at any given moment is maintained, not because their free energy is at a minimum as in thermodynamic equilibrium, but because the systems are continually receiving free energy from the surrounding medium in an amount which compensates for its decrease in the systems. For such chemical open systems as the coacervate droplets of the primaeval hydrosphere, the intake of free energy from the external medium was mainly brought about by the entry of organic compounds relatively rich in energy into the droplet and their participation in some chemical reaction within it. However, when chemical reactions are going on, closed and open systems differ kinetically from one another in that, in the former, equilibrium is maintained by the equality of the rates of reaction in the forward and reverse directions, and, therefore, it follows that there cannot be any increase in their mass. In open systems in the stationary state, on the other hand, the rate of reaction in one direction is regularly greater than in the other and, accordingly it is possible for there to be such an integration of reactions within such systems as would lead to an increase in the mass of the system. Such systems had an undoubted advantage in the process of oriented evolution and therefore, owing to the action of ' selection ' they occupied a dominant position among the organised formations which were coming into being.

Droplets of artificial static coacervates cannot divide spontaneously. On the contrary, the forces of surface tension tend to cause them to coalesce and it is only the presence of a surface film which, to some extent, averts this.

However, as we know, fragmentation may be brought about even in such static systems by external influences, such as simple shaking in making an emulsion. The earliest growing coacervates might have been divided in some such way (for example by the action of breaking waves). In droplets which already had the characteristics of a dynamic stationary system, the existence of which was dependent on the processes going on inside it, their division could have been evoked by internal causes. For example, it could occur when the internal osmotic pressure rose so quickly, owing to the hydrolysis of compounds of high molecular weight, that it became too great for the outer layer of the droplet to contain.

Thus, as a result of the constant interaction of the original systems discussed above with the external medium, there was a gradual increase in the number of these systems. However, this increase always took place under the strict control of a ' selection ' which only retained for further evolution the most effective systems, so that the quality of their organisation was always changing in a particular direction. The systems began to be not only dynamically stable but actually dynamic. We may regard this phenomenon as the third important step in the orientated evolution towards the origin of life.

In the first stages of the evolution with which we are concerned, we may imagine the fate of any single individual coacervate droplet apart from its connection with any other such droplets, the overriding consideration governing the continued existence of the particular droplet as an open system, for its self-preservation in a condition of continual interaction with the external medium, is the relationship between the rates of the processes taking place within it and not the absolute magnitude of those rates.

It can be shown by direct laboratory experiment that when there are several, parallel, chemical stationary systems with a common external medium, the greatest flow of material takes place through the system whose organisation (e.g. the presence of effective catalysts) ensures the greatest over-all rate of chemical transformation. In view of this, the chemical stationary system which achieves the fastest chemical processes under given conditions will have an advantage over other parallel stationary systems so long as the increased rate does not upset the balance necessary for its self-preservation, that is, if it is compatible with the prolonged existence of the open system concerned.

One can thus see that a dynamic, stable, coacervate droplet which can preserve itself and grow and which has acquired, by interaction with the external medium, the ability to transform substances more quickly has, at the same time, obtained a considerable advantage over other droplets suspended in the same solution of organic and inorganic compounds, but carrying out their own characteristic chemical processes more slowly.

These more dynamic drops will come to represent a higher and higher proportion of the total mass of the coacervate. There will be competition between the droplets based on the rate at which processes take place within them and the rate at which they grow.

However, it must be noted that the power of self-preservation and even rapid growth of all dynamic systems does not imply complete immutability of that system. On the contrary, a stationary coacervate droplet, or any other open system, can maintain its integrity for a long time, while continually changing its composition and the network of reactions going on within it, so long as these changes do not upset its dynamic stability. Changes of this sort must, in fact, have happened on the way to the origin of life, as the progressive evolution of the original systems depended on them. Without these changes no new subjects would have arisen for natural selection and further development of the systems which would have been ' frozen ' at some particular stage.

THE ORIGIN OF THE FIRST ORGANISMS

However, it was naturally extremely important that these changes should not stray beyond the limits of compatibility with the dynamic stability of the system. If they did so there would be such a forcible upset of the equilibrium that there would always be the risk of the system losing its stability and disappearing. Thus, when the original systems were extending quickly and massively, the only ones selected for further evolution were those in which the reactions of the network were co-ordinated in such a way that there developed constantly repeated chains, or even closed cycles of reactions, in which the reactions always followed the same cycle and it was only at definite points on it that branching occurred. This ensured the constant repetition of the formation of new amounts of particular metabolic products.

It was out of this constancy of the repetition of inter-related reactions, co-ordinated into a single network, that there arose that power of self-reproduction which is characteristic of living bodies. One may speak of the moment when this arose as the moment of the origin of life. At this stage in the evolution of matter, natural selection acquired its full biological significance and on its basis there began to develop a higher and higher degree of adaptation of organisms to the conditions of their existence and the precise correspondence of all the details of their internal structure to the functions performed by them. This was, in fact, the development of that striking ' purposiveness ' of the structure of living bodies of which we have already talked.

Each of the steps, to which we have referred, on the road to the development of life, has been associated with progressive improvement in the organisation of metabolism. Individual reactions, which were originally sporadic, became linked into chains which then grew longer and longer, branched and closed up into cycles. Individual chains and cycles became integrated into an ever more elaborate and efficient metabolic network. In it the constantly repeated, synthetic reactions were closely interwoven with the destructive reactions of decomposition which produced the energy required for synthesis as well as the molecular fragments from which were formed a host of specific substances and the multimolecular structures developing out of them. This formation followed standard lines fixed by the process of selection in the long and complicated metabolic chains.

Thus, in close unison with the development of the metabolic

network of the evolving system there was a continual increase in complexity and efficiency of both their chemical composition and their spatial organisation. Both of these gave rise to more orderly metabolic sequences of reactions but, at the same time, they determined the actual establishment and improvement of this orderliness.

The rates of the reactions occurring in the coacervate droplets which were originally formed in the hydrosphere can, at first, have depended only on the catalytic activity of those inorganic salts of iron, copper, calcium etc. which were widespread in the surrounding medium and on the various organic radicals contained in the droplet. Salts and radicals of this sort have a comparatively weak catalytic activity and, more important still, it is very non-specific. The co-ordination of the separate reactions in the original coacervate systems, being based on such activities, can, therefore, not have been very effective.

However, as we now know, the strength and specificity of catalytic activity can be increased considerably by the presence of particular combinations of substances or groups of atoms. For example, if an atom of iron unites with porphyrin, which is part of the red pigment of blood, then the catalytic activity of the combination becomes about a thousand times as great as that of inorganic iron alone. Not only that, but there is a considerable increase in the specificity of such a combined catalyst.

In coacervate droplets interacting with their external medium, many combinations of substances may occur, some successful and others unsuccessful from the point of view of their catalytic strength and specificity. However, only the former will be fixed and maintained by selection, as droplets possessing them will obtain a considerable advantage in respect of the further improvement of their metabolic network.

In modern enzymes, which manifest themselves as strictly organised centres of catalytic activity in protein molecules, evolution has already achieved a very high level of efficiency. This efficient close connection between the molecular structure of an enzyme and its biological function could, naturally, not have arisen by ' chance '. It required a regulated and orientated process of development, determined by a selection which destroyed all unsuccessful combinations and only kept, for further development, those coacervate systems in which the catalytic apparatus fulfilled its biological function most rationally.

Enzymes, however, only represent the original and simplest form of the organisation of protoplasm, its separate working parts. Taken by itself, the individual enzymic reaction cannot serve as a basis for a vital process. Its biological significance only appears when it is included as an indispensable link in the common metabolic network. Selection was therefore directed, not only to the perfection of any single enzyme or of a few enzymes, but to the rational organisation of the catalysts themselves and of other factors regulating metabolism. On this basis there arose proteins as well as other substances of strictly determinate structure such, for example, as nucleic acids.

Grouping together of all these substances led to the formation of protoplasmic structures, regularly constructed aggregates having energetic, synthetic and structure-determining functions. For reasons given above, their concerted and co-ordinated activities were continually directed towards the constant self-preservation and self-reproduction of the whole living system under the given conditions of the external medium.

Thus, we can already imagine, though only in its barest outlines, the course of development leading from the original systems to the most primitive organisms. This course led through progressive improvements in the network of reactions in individual colloidal systems interacting with their external environment. Owing to the continual changing of these systems, within the limits of their dynamic stability, and to the continual action of selection, it was only the most efficient which survived. These underwent the following reorganisation. In the first place the individual catalysts were improved, acquiring greater activity and specificity. In parallel with this, there was a temporal co-ordination of these activities and whole chains and cycles of enzymic reactions began to occur, forming the basis for the different departments of metabolism. Further improvement of the spatial organisation and localisation of processes also took place and there was a rationalisation of the interdependent energetic and constructive branches of metabolism guaranteeing, within certain limits, the continued survival and self-reproduction of the living system.

Natural selection has long ago wiped from the face of the Earth all intermediate forms of organisation between the original coacervates and the most primitive living things. We, therefore, have no possibility of studying them under natural conditions. However, the picture we have drawn of orderly evolution on the way to the origin of life is not purely hypothetical. It is based on a study of the chemical mechanisms which are now being discovered in living bodies and isolated fragments of them, and also on the construction of artificial systems such as complex coacervate droplets containing enzymic proteins and other simple and complicated catalysts. But we get far more help in this direction from a comparative study of the metabolism of contemporary organisms at different stages of evolutionary development.

Just as an anatomist makes a comparative study of the individual organs of different animals and can thus produce a chart of their evolution, so the biochemist can make a comparative study of the metabolism of various organisms and thus approach the very source of life and understand the most primitive forms of its organisation.

Only by an evolutionary approach of this sort shall we reach a position from which we shall be able to understand not only *what* happens in the living body and *how* it happens but also give answers to the 7 million *whys* which lie between us and a true understanding of the essence of life.

THE EARLIEST PERIOD OF THE DEVELOPMENT OF LIFE

' Dich im Unendlichen zu finden
Musst unterscheiden und dann verbinden.'*

GOETHE

THE HISTORY OF THE EARTH

FROM an isotope analysis of lead, and other studies of radioactive materials, the age of the Earth as a planet has been set at about 5,000,000,000 years. This means that if one were to try to record the history of the Earth in 10 volumes of 500 pages each, every page would cover a period of a million years. The British geologist Marr once said that we can only make a connected study of the tenth and last of these volumes. The fossilised remains of animals and plants which have been preserved since the Cambrian era enable us to get a clear idea of the irreversible process of development of the organic world which has been going on without interruption for the past 500,000,000 years. The succession of important stages in the long path of development of life is so accurately represented in the palaeontological records of this period that the process as a whole can serve as a valuable chronometer with the help of which geologists determine the time of origin of the sedimentary deposits which they are studying.

As we turn over successively the leaves of this book, making a chronological study of the important events which enrich the story of the development of the organic world over the last 500 million years, we immediately become aware of the steady increase in the tempo of this development.

At first it took place relatively slowly so that, for example, almost half the period under discussion was required before

---

* Thee in the infinite to find,
Must separate and then combine.

plants could become fully terrestrial while, on the sea-shore and in swamps, amphibious animals crawled out on to the land while still retaining their complete dependence on water, in which they spawned and which was necessary to them for the continual moistening of their easily-dried skin.

The further evolution of terrestrial animals took place considerably more quickly. However, it was a further 100 million years before reptiles became dominant and these reached the height of their development only 60-70 million years ago. Only half that time, 35 million years, passed before the predominance of the reptiles was superseded by that of the birds and beasts and these acquired the structural features we see to-day only about 5-7 million years ago. The entire history of man is confined to the very last page of our book.

The great and continually increasing pace of the development of life during this period has accounted for the amazing variety of highly developed plants and animals in the world around us. But, of course, the beginning of life did not by any means coincide with the beginning of our tenth volume. On the contrary, even in its very first pages we meet numerous multicellular algae and invertebrate animals such as medusae, worms, echinoderms, molluscs and trilobites. The only ones missing are the vertebrates. However, the plants and animals mentioned are, comparatively speaking, very highly organised living things which could only have arisen as a result of the very prolonged development of life on the Earth beforehand.

Even comparatively recently it was believed that the palaeontological record was cut off at the Cambrian and that remains of animals which inhabited the Earth more than 500 million years ago had not been preserved, as the rock formations in which they were incorporated had suffered profound alteration and metamorphosis which completely destroyed all biogenic structures. However, it has recently been established that at many points on the surface of the globe, especially on such platforms as the Russian, the Siberian and the Chinese, below the strata containing the most ancient Cambrian complex of fossils there are, closely associated with these strata, very slightly altered strata which are sometimes extremely thick. Study of these formations has only been begun comparatively recently, but it has already been possible to find in them many fossils preserved from pre-Cambrian times. It is true that there are no fossilised remains of animals of any sort, but the vegetable kingdom is represented in these formations by fragments and accumulations of various kinds of branching and unicellular algae, especially blue-green ones, and by spores of some other primitive plants. Thus there stands before our eyes an epoch of life preceding the Cambrian era, which has recently been given the name of the Riffian era. There is much evidence to show that this era was as long as the palaeozoic, mesozoic and cainozoic ages put together. It began more than a thousand million years ago and occupied a tremendous length of time, more than has passed from the palaeozoic age to the present time.

The Riffian era thus occupies the whole of the ninth volume of our history of the development of the world and maybe part of the eighth as well. Unfortunately many of the pages of this book have been considerably damaged by time, many of them have been completely lost and the order of others has been disturbed and distorted. In particular, people have come to the conclusion that, in many cases, the strata of the Riffian rocks contain vegetable fragments and spores of far more recent origin than would be deduced from the geological evidence. For instance, even in the proterozoic formations which are more ancient than the Riffian, people have found spores characteristic of the highly developed plants of the Carboniferous period, which was only 250 million years ago. It is clear that these spores must have been transferred in some way from the overlying strata and do not, in any way, represent proterozoic life. One must therefore be specially careful to take account of the fact that there are accidental and non-systematic finds of individual fragments of plants in the Riffian strata. The age of these finds is far from always corresponding with that of the formations in which they occur.

Nevertheless we can already give some account of the characteristics of the development of life during the Riffian era, even though these may be only very generalised and approximate. Here we do not find the striking variety of form which is characteristic of our own time and which could only develop at a later epoch. The evolution of life flowed less rapidly in the Riffian than it did after the Cambrian period. In the Riffian, evolution was mainly directed to the perfection of intracellular organisation and development of multicellularity.

THE DEVELOPMENT OF LIFE UP TO THE FORMATION OF CELLS

However, even at the beginning of the Riffian era there obviously existed plants which were capable of photosynthesis even though they were very primitive. As we now know, photosynthesis requires the presence of a very highly differentiated internal apparatus which could only have been formed over a long period after the origin of life and only as a result of the protracted evolution of the first living things. Thus, in trying to discover the beginnings of life we shall have to dig down into an even more ancient period of the existence of our planet, that is to say, into the proterozoic era. However, in the formations belonging to this period we have only a few individual, accidental findings of structural remains of life and can only infer its existence and nature from indirect evidence such as geochemical data, in particular deposits of oxidised iron, very ancient deposits of limestone and also graphite and pre-Cambrian coals. The significance of these findings can be interpreted in different ways. For example, oxidised iron need not necessarily have arisen as a result of the formation of oxygen by photosynthesis, but might have arisen by the full oxidation of the ferrous salts dissolved in the sea water by the oxygen which was formed abiogenically by the photochemical splitting of water in the superficial layers of the atmosphere. Naturally, this decomposition only occurred on a small scale but, all the same, it could have gone on for very long periods of time.

Similarly, it is only in a very few cases that the distribution of the carbon isotopes can be used to give us an idea as to whether a deposit is of primary abiogenic origin or is secondary. There is, however, no method which can give the answer to the question as to whether a given deposit was derived from the organic material of the ' primaeval broth ', from coacervate droplets or from formed living things, that is to say, decide whether they were laid down before or after the origin of life.

Thus, we do not yet possess the direct, factual evidence which would enable us to set a more or less definite time for the origin of life. However, the fact, which we have already mentioned more than once, that the evolution of life gets faster and faster the more advanced it is, and that the earliest stages of its evolution must have required considerably greater periods of time than did the later ones, justify us in assuming that the length of the earliest period of the development of life was not less, but possibly greater, than the length of all the succeeding periods put together.

From what has been said we can (though only very tentatively, of course) set out the following chapter headings for our complete history of the Earth. The greater number of its pages (about six volumes) would be concerned with the lifeless period of the existence of our planet. During this time there occurred the multitudinous processes which we described in the previous chapter. They were tangled together in a complicated skein and were very poorly organised, so they could only develop slowly but they brought about the gradual increase in complexity of organic substances, their polymerisation, the formation of coacervate droplets and, at last, the transformation of these into the first living things. Only the last four volumes are left to deal with the whole of the development of life. During a good proportion of the time covered by these volumes (probably a good half), life was represented on the Earth by organisms which had a considerably less highly organised internal structure than any which we can see around us to-day. Between the organisms which first arose from coacervate droplets and the most primitive organisms of the Riffian period there lay a long road of gradual improvement of metabolic processes and protoplasmic structures, a road with many stages representing the successive development of those new qualities which now form the basis of the organisation of living matter. What innumerable and multifarious chemical mechanisms, what endless combinations of metabolic reactions between their chains and cycles must have occurred in that time, which must have been at least one thousand million years; and how many of these combinations and mechanisms must have been eliminated and destroyed by natural selection, not because they violated the laws of physics or chemistry, but because they were not sufficiently ' purposive ', because they were less well adapted than other similar processes to the fulfilment of the vital functions required by the organism under the given conditions of its existence.

If we once fully grasp the whole grandiosity of this evolution, how laughable and naive we shall find the hopeless attempts which have been made, even quite recently, to reproduce artificially the spontaneous birth of life, in putrefying broths and infusions of organic materials. The path followed by nature from the first organisms to the most primitive bacteria or algae was certainly neither shorter nor simpler than that from the amoeba to man. But naturally nobody now sets himself the task of making a man out of masses of unicellular creatures. Perhaps, when speaking of the synthesis of life, we should now think, not of the construction of cells like those of the present, which are capable of respiration or photosynthesis and which we usually study, but of the artificial reproduction of comparatively less complicated systems which, nevertheless, have most of the fundamental characteristics of living things, namely, the ability to carry out metabolic processes, even though only relatively primitive ones, which will yet ensure their continual self-preservation and self-reproduction under the existing environmental conditions of the surrounding medium. Clearly we can only envisage the possible features of such systems on the basis of a study of the origin and subsequent development of life. For this reason the very earliest period of the development of life is of special importance to an understanding of its essential nature for, it was just at this time that the fundamental properties common to all living things were being established.

But what are the facts on which to base our study of this period in the history of the evolution of life? As we have already indicated, there are, of course, no fossils incontrovertibly dating from that time. And even if such fossils were to be found, they would not tell us very much, for the beginning of the evolution of life was essentially concerned with the improvement of the metabolism of living bodies and the finest details of their internal structure rather than with changes in the outward form of the primitive organisms.

We have already discussed the most ancient periods of the evolution of matter which preceded the origin of life, basing our discussion on a conviction of the absolute constancy and immutability of the laws of physics and chemistry. When methane, ammonia, hydrogen and water react together under particular conditions in our laboratories to form amino acids, then we are convinced that such compounds must also have arisen on the surface of the Earth, thousands of millions of years ago, before the origin of life, if the conditions prevailing in the atmosphere of our planet at that time resembled those which we now reproduce artificially. Once life has come into being, however, the laws of physics and chemistry alone are not enough to determine the course of the further evolution of matter: An understanding of this course can now only be achieved on the basis of the new biological laws which developed concurrently with life.

Each essential link in the metabolic chain can, from the purely chemical point of view, be brought about by a very large number of related chemical processes none of which would, in any way, violate the laws of physics or chemistry. In the process of the development of life, however, natural selection has preserved for further development only a few individual combinations of reactions out of all these numerous chemical possibilities. These were then transferred from one generation to the next. We are far from always able to understand why this happened to one particular combination or chemical mechanism, as a purely chemical approach would always show that other combinations were equally good. In such cases the matter is clearly determined by some historic necessity, some specific biological adaptation. It is, however, important, that the further use of these particular biologically selected collections and mechanisms, rather than any others which were chemically possible, became as obligatory in the whole subsequent development of the living world as the constancy of chemical reactions or physical processes is in the world of inorganic things.

We can now find, in particular metabolic sequences, sets of reactions which appear to be common to all organisms without exception. It follows that these combinations which developed as a result of the action of natural selection, being selected from the immense multitude of other chemically possible combinations, already existed at the time when the ' tree of life ' had not yet thrown out its numerous independent branches. Thus these metabolic sequences are now carried out by the same combinations of chemical events which realised them many hundreds of millions of years ago.

As we shall see later, this constancy of biological organisation has nothing in common with the static unchangingness of ' clockwork ' or of an ' aperiodic crystal ', as Schroedinger would describe living things. The dynamic basis of this constancy, its connection with the flowing character of the organisation of living things, is quite self-evident. Here, however, we must particularly emphasise the fact that this constancy cannot be determined by the general laws of chemical kinetics or thermodynamics alone. It is the expression of a form of organisation which could only have been elaborated historically in the process of the development of living material.

Thus the property of living bodies which we have noticed takes on the character of a specific biological law. An understanding of this law will enable us to use increasingly detailed comparative biochemical analysis of the metabolism of modern organisms as a basis for tracing the evolutionary paths followed by the living world many hundreds of millions of years ago, just as we use the general laws of physics and chemistry in trying to understand the processes of development of organic material which preceded the appearance of life.

Of course, there is no doubt that the particular collection of chemical reactions constituting the most ancient metabolism, which arose at the actual sources of life, have been repeatedly supplemented, improved and made more complicated in the course of its further evolution, especially in connection with changes in the external conditions with which the organism was continually interacting. The changes came about in different ways in the groups of organisms which had already become differentiated from one another. Thus, the evolution of metabolism did not proceed along a single straight line any more than did the far more recent evolution of morphological form of higher plants and animals. It pursued winding paths which often interlaced with one another and branched to form a complicated ' tree ' of different types of metabolism. Many of the branches of this ' tree ' have withered and vanished long ago, leaving no trace behind them, while others have come down to our own times but the link between them which once existed has now been practically lost and can only be understood by means of a far deeper analysis of the available facts.

All this paints a rather complicated and confusing picture of the earliest evolution of life. This picture is still very incomplete, especially because people have only very recently begun to study the factual evidence and because people still do not realise how much has already been done by evolutionary biochemistry in this direction. However, as we can see from a comparative study of the processes of biological formation of proteins and nucleic acids, the chemical mechanisms of fermentation, respiration, photo- and chemosynthesis and other vital phenomena in various micro-organisms and in higher plants and animals, the new sets of biochemical reactions which were always arising did not, by any means, always completely replace the older metabolic processes but usually made use of them, simply supplementing them with newly developed reactions. The newly formed sets of reactions were very often only what might be called accessory superstructures on the previously existing internal chemical mechanisms of living bodies. In some sectors of the metabolism, in a number of organisms, we can even observe the presence of two parallel paths of chemical transformation, the newer of which is extensively used in metabolism while the older acts, as it were, as a reserve. It is, however, retained intact and therefore organisms which possess it may sometimes, when there is a serious change in the conditions of their existence, easily return to the older form of metabolism.

Some relatively simple and poorly developed sets of metabolic reactions are actually the same in all contemporary living things. However, the more complicated combinations of these sets of reactions may vary, differing in some degree from one of the main biological groups to another but always keeping the same universal foundations. As well as this we can observe chemical mechanisms which are peculiar to and used by only particular limited groups of living things while other groups do not have them. This enables us to find our way to some extent in the complicated labyrinth of repeatedly branching paths of biochemical evolution and, in some cases, even to establish the time or the order of the origins of particular links or whole chains and cycles in the general complicated network of metabolic reactions. If, for example, we find that a given system of biochemical reactions is peculiar to a particular more or less limited group of organisms and is absent from all other living things, if it is only an auxiliary part of the metabolism of the organism in question while a more widely distributed set of reactions forms the basis of the chemical mechanism of the vital phenomenon in which it takes part and, finally, if, in some cases, when affected by certain influences or conditions, it can be suspended and the metabolism will then follow a new path without necessarily leading to the destruction of the organism, then we are justified in regarding such a system as relatively young, having only arisen at a rather late stage in the course of phylogenetic development. On the other hand, if, in the course of our comparative study of the metabolism of various organisms we find one and the same set of reactions and metabolic mechanisms common to all living beings, then we are justified in regarding these systems and mechanisms as being extremely ancient, lying at the very roots of the organisation of the ' tree of life '.

THE FIRST LIVING THINGS WERE ANAEROBIC HETEROTROPHS

In this way, by trying to detect in the tremendous variety of systems of metabolism in different organisms those similarities, those features of organisation which are most widespread among all living things, and therefore most ancient, we can, in the first place, establish two cardinal principles.

First, the metabolism of all contemporary living things is based on systems which are designed for the utilisation of ready-made organic substances as their primary building material for biosynthesis and as the source of that energy which is necessary for life although one might, theoretically, postulate many other satisfactory metabolic pathways.

In the second place, all contemporary living organisms have a biochemical system for obtaining energy from organic substances which is based on the anaerobic degradation of these substances although, with free oxygen in the atmosphere, as it is now, it would be perfectly rational for them to be oxidised directly.

It is self-evident and generally accepted that the overwhelming majority of the biological species which now inhabit our planet can only exist if they are constantly supplied with ready-made organic substances. This applies to all animals, both higher and lower, including most of the protozoa, the great majority of bacteria and all fungi. This fact alone is extremely suggestive. One can hardly imagine that all these evolved simply as Batesonian simplifications, as a complete loss of the autotrophic abilities which they once had. This is also contradicted by the intensive biochemical studies of the metabolic systems of these organisms. We do not find in them the least trace or vestige of those specific enzymic complexes or groups of reactions which are required by autotrophic forms of life while, on the other hand, the metabolism of autotrophs is always based on the same internal chemical mechanisms as that of all those other organisms which can only exist by consuming organic substances. The specific autotrophic mechanisms are merely superstructures on this foundation. It is just this sort of organisation of their metabolisms which allows autotrophs, under certain conditions, to revert entirely to the consumption of ready-made organic substances.

This can be demonstrated particularly clearly in the case of the least highly organised photoautotrophs—the algae— both in natural conditions and in the laboratory. By means of such experiments it has long ago been shown that if organic substances are introduced into sterile cultures of algae they will assimilate these substances directly. This may go on at the same time as photosynthesis but, in some cases, photosynthesis may stop altogether and the alga go over to a completely saprophytic way of life.

Under these conditions one gets a very luxuriant growth of blue-green algae such as *Nostoc* and the diatoms as well as such green algae as, for example, *Spirogyra*. Many forms of blue-green and other algae must obviously assimilate organic compounds directly even under natural conditions, when they live in dirty ponds. This is suggested by the fact that they grow especially luxuriantly in stagnant waters and other such places where organic substances abound.

A heterotrophic basis for nutrition may be found, not only in the algae, but also in higher plants, although their photosynthetic apparatus has here reached the acme of its development. It is, however, only present in the chlorophyll-bearing cells of higher plants, the metabolism of all the rest of the tissues, which are colourless, is based, like that of all other living things, on the use of the organic substances supplied to them, in this case, by the photosynthetic organs. Furthermore, even leaves revert to this form of metabolism when they are without light.

Thus the metabolism of all higher plants is entirely based on the heterotrophic mechanism of assimilation of organic substances, but in the green tissues this mechanism is accompanied by a supplementary, specific superstructure which has the task of supplying the whole organism with ready-made organic substances. If these substances reach the plant from outside in one way or another, then it can exist even without its photosynthetic superstructure, as may be observed under normal, natural conditions, especially in the germination of seeds. This may also be demonstrated artificially in cultures of vegetable tissues or in the growing of a complete adult plant of sugar beet in the dark from roots grown the previous year. In these cases either a complete higher plant or its tissues live in the total absence of any activity by their photosynthetic apparatus by the assimilation of exogenous organic substances. If, however, one breaks even one link in the chain of heterotrophic metabolism (by introducing a specific inhibitor, for example) then all the vital activities of the plant are brought to a standstill and it is destroyed.

Hence it is perfectly clear that the vital processes of the photoautotrophs are founded on the original and ancient form of metabolism based on the use of ready made organic substances and that they developed the power of photosynthesis considerably later, as an accessory to their earlier heterotrophic metabolic mechanism.

The same may be said of that narrower group of autotrophs, the chemoautotrophs, although it might seem, at first glance, that things are somewhat more complicated in this case. Even in the times of S. Vinogradskiĭ, the discoverer of these organisms, they were held to be the first living things to make their appearance on the Earth and to have the most primitive form of metabolism.

The basis of this idea was the belief, prevalent at that time, that, under natural conditions, organic material can only arise biogenically, through the agency of organisms, and that the organisms which first appeared on the Earth must therefore have been able to exist without organic nutriment, on purely mineral media. The chemoautotrophs are just such organisms, they can synthesise organic substances themselves using only carbon dioxide as their source of carbon, obtaining the energy they need by the oxidation of reduced inorganic substances such as ammonia, hydrogen sulphide, ferrous iron or molecular hydrogen.

We now know, however, that, during the evolution of our planet, organic substances arose on its surface abiogenically long before the appearance of the first organisms. These need not, therefore, necessarily have been autotrophic. Also, the further we progress in our study of the metabolism of the various chemoautotrophs, the clearer it becomes that this metabolism is by no means simpler, but, on the contrary, is more complicated than that of related heterotrophic organisms. In particular it has recently been shown that the metabolism of chemoautotrophs is also based on the system of reactions of decomposition and synthesis of organic compounds common to all other organisms, while the processes of oxidation of inorganic substances are only accessory supplements to these systems. The overwhelming majority of chemoautotrophs, like the photoautotrophs, can, therefore, easily revert to the assimilation of organic material and only a few of them are ' strictly ' chemoautotrophs, being unable, for some still ill-understood reasons, to abstract organic substances from the external medium. Nevertheless, even these ' strict ' chemo-autotrophs, such as *Thiobacillus thiooxidans*, can break down intracellular deposits of polysaccharides in the course of their metabolism, and the same enzymic apparatus underlies this transformation and the same sequence of reactions is followed as in heterotrophs.

Thus, the metabolism of all autotrophs is based on a biochemical apparatus for the transformation of organic substances. It is the most primitive and general and, therefore, also the earliest apparatus, while the photosynthetic and chemosynthetic apparatuses attach themselves to it as supplementary, complicating, secondary and therefore more recent superstructures.

Similarly the anaerobic method of energy metabolism may easily be shown to be primary by means of an extensive biochemical analysis of the processes taking place in all groups of contemporary organisms, both higher and lower. It is true that most of these organisms now lead an aerobic life and that there is only a very limited number of relatively primitive creatures living at present which do not need free oxygen at all, or can live for a long time without this gas. This state of affairs is quite understandable. Respiration is an incomparably more rational process than anaerobic metabolism. Therefore, no sooner did free oxygen appear in the atmosphere of the Earth than organisms, in the course of their evolution, must have become very extensively adapted to the aerobic way of life. Nevertheless, the energy metabolism of all organisms, without exception, is based on chains of reactions which are remarkably alike and which are not associated with the use of free oxygen but involve the same complicated collection of enzymic processes which also occur in modern anaerobes. The reaction of oxidation by free oxygen, which is specific to aerobes, only supplements the common anaerobic mechanism; the oxidative 'superstructures', unlike the anaerobic basic mechanism, can vary considerably from organism to organism. Thus, for example, the oxidative enzymes which are characteristic of plants are absent not only from anaerobes, but also from animals which, although they respire, possess their own aerobic mechanisms.

Such a state of affairs would be quite incomprehensible if life had arisen under conditions in which the atmosphere was oxidative and contained free oxygen. Under such conditions the earliest and, therefore, the most general mechanisms of energy metabolism would necessarily have been aerobic ones while the mechanisms of 'life without oxygen', e.g. alcoholic fermentation and glycolysis, would have been peculiar to anaerobes which had developed at some later stage of evolution by a regressive loss of their original respiratory mechanisms.

In fact, as we have seen, the situation is quite the opposite. The trunk of the 'tree of life' is based on a collection of anaerobic reactions while the respiratory mechanisms attached themselves to it later, after the trunk had become divided into branches.

The results of this evolutionary biochemical analysis are, perhaps, one of the most convincing demonstrations that life arose on the Earth under conditions where the atmosphere and hydrosphere were reducing. In just the same way, the facts we have already discussed concerning the heterotrophic basis of nutrition lead us to believe that the original sources of both energy and structural materials for the first living things were the organic substances in the surrounding medium which had arisen abiogenically.

As we make a deeper study of the details of the chemical organisation of the vital phenomena in different representatives of the animal and vegetable world and especially of various micro-organisms, we can try to sketch out a reasonably credible picture of the successive developments in metabolism and the elaboration of the internal structure of living bodies, that is to say, the processes which took place at the very beginning of life, about 2,000,000,000 years ago.

According to what was said in the previous chapter, what emerged from the evolution described there must have been systems formed of protein-like and other high-molecular organic substances, immersed in the abiogenically developing ' nutrient broth ', separated from this external medium by some sort of surface interface but continually interacting with the medium in such a way that, in spite of the continuous processes of disintegration, they constantly remained capable of self-preservation and self-reproduction.

If we are to avoid some mistakes which are rather common in the scientific literature we should now emphasise two important facts.

In the first place, the sequence of the abiogenic synthetic reactions which took place in the external medium or ' primary nutrient broth ' is often represented as being much the same as the sequence occurring in biosynthesis within contemporary living bodies. This is fundamentally wrong. Owing to the specific organisation of living bodies, the biosynthetic sequence is directed towards a particular aim and proceeds along the path of a strictly determined sequence of reactions. This can therefore lead to the constant production of very complicated and specific substances which can therefore quickly accumulate and reach a considerable concentration in the cell. In the

' primary broth ' the synthesis of organic substances took place in quite a different way, as we can show directly by comparing the biosynthesis of amino acids with Miller's synthesis or the formation of proteins with Akabori's synthesis. In the ' primary broth ' the syntheses did not follow any determinate paths of reactions which were strictly co-ordinated with one another, but wandered in all directions over the extremely wide field of chemical possibilities where individual reactions intersected each other in a completely haphazard way. Thus there could develop in it a tremendous variety of all possible forms of organic compounds and polymers, but the more complicated and specific any particular substance was, the greater the number of reactions which must have taken part in its formation, this therefore became less probable and the possible concentration of this particular substance in the ' primaeval broth ' was correspondingly less. One may therefore suppose that there was an extensive abiogenic formation of sugars, amino acids, purine bases and non-specific polymers of these substances, namely, polypeptides and polynucleotides. However, as we have shown above, it is hardly likely that there was any abiogenic formation of proteins and nucleic acids with a strictly correlated disposition of amino acid and mononucleotide residues. The development of the less complicated, but yet specifically constructed substances characteristic of modern protoplasm in the ' primaeval broth ' is more probable, but their concentration in it can only have been minute.

The second error which is very common in the scientific literature is the view, held by many scientists and discussed by us in Chapter I, that the origin of the first organism was rather like the assembly of some machine from prefabricated components. The external medium is then regarded as a reserve store of such components so that the only thing that could have occurred in the formation of the organism in the original medium was the selection of components in accordance with the one and only correct plan for the construction of any particular living thing. Of course there never was and never could have been any such plan. The first organisms were similar in their chemical composition to the medium which surrounded them, not because this was very complicated and specific (as many scientists now believe) but, on the contrary, because the composition and structure of the living things from which biological evolution started was incomparably simpler than that of the living things we see in nature around us.

The primitive composition and structure of the original organisms must have changed an incalculable number of times and an incalculable number of the variants produced must have been rejected and irrevocably annihilated.

Only gradually, by a process of natural selection, were those features of composition and organisation, which we find in all contemporary organisms, established. However, the state of our knowledge is such that we are still far from being able to declare that just these particular details of organisation and not others are absolutely necessary for the existence of any conceivable living being. On the contrary, as has been shown above, if our approach to the question were purely physical or chemical we should have no hesitation in giving a negative answer. Historically, however, particular forms of organisation were elaborated at some early stage of the development of life and, in accordance with biological laws, they became common to all living things. If we are to understand them we must therefore understand the process of their establishment.

The simplest scheme representing the systems from which life originated has already been represented thus:—

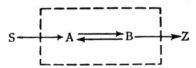

The most important structural element of such a system is the surface separating it from the surrounding medium. This could have been a simple interface between a coacervate droplet and its equilibrium liquid; it could also have been a formation with a far more complicated structure, for example, a protein-lipid film like the micellar formations constructed in the form of a sandwich, which were found by Bungenberg de Jong on the surfaces of coacervates which he made from gelatin and potassium oleate. In these films there was a layer of orientated molecules of oleic acid between two unimolecular layers of protein. It is important to note that a membrane consisting of bimolecular sheets of lipids, more or less closely bound to protein on the watery side of the separating membrane is the most general structural element in all living bodies, which indicates that it arose very early in the process of the evolution of life.

The permeability and adsorptive properties of membranes vary according to their composition, structure and charge and even in the simplest coacervates, obtained artificially, they have a selective character. Thus some substances from the surrounding solution scarcely enter into the droplets, while others accumulate there in greater concentrations than in the external medium. If the substances which enter into the droplet do not undergo any chemical change there, a steady thermodynamic equilibrium is set up, sooner or later, between the droplet and the external medium.

If the droplet is to have the character of an open system there must be a continuous flow of energy into it from the external medium such that $dF =$ constant. In the case of a system suspended in a solution of organic substances which can enter into it, the easiest way of obtaining energy from the external medium is by means of the process which may be represented diagrammatically as the reaction $A \rightleftharpoons B$.

The substance A, which is continually arriving in the system from the external medium, is transformed into substance B with the liberation of a definite amount of energy (exoergically). Substance B then diffuses out into the external medium. This ensures a constant flow of energy through the system always in the same direction. One may conceive of an infinite number of such reactions, leading to the giving off of free energy, occurring in the ' primaeval broth ' but the most effective of them, in the presence of a reducing hydrosphere, would undoubtedly be oxido-reductive reactions, i.e. processes associated with the transfer of hydrogen or of an electron.

VARIOUS FORMS OF METABOLISM

It is clear that it was reactions of just this sort which were the first metabolic processes in the developing metabolism. This follows from the purely physico-chemical considerations discussed above and also from comparative biochemical studies, which demonstrate that these processes are obligatory for all living beings without exception.

On the basis of the collection of a very large quantity of relevant factual material A. Kluyver has written as follows: " Thus we arrive at the conclusion that the most essential characteristic of the living state is the existence in parts of the cell of a continuous movement of electrons in one direction ".

Oxido-reductive reactions, especially reactions involving the transfer of hydrogen, may involve the splitting of molecules or, on the other hand, their condensation. This may be represented by the following scheme:—

$$AH+B \rightarrow A+BH$$
$$AHB \rightarrow A+BH$$
$$AH+B \rightarrow ABH$$

As a consequence of these reactions the concentrations of the substances entering the system (those shown on the left) is continually falling while that of the products of the reaction (shown on the right) is rising. This is a prerequisite for the movement of substances in one direction through the system. In fact such movement will only take place when the rate at which the reaction proceeds inside the system is greater than that at which it can proceed in the external medium. For this it is necessary that there should be some sort of catalyst within the system (either arising or accumulating there) which can accelerate the reaction concerned, even though only slightly. If we approach the subject from a purely physico-chemical point of view we can imagine an enormous number of groups of atoms, radicals or organic or inorganic compounds which might fulfil this requirement.

It is, however, very significant that, out of these multitudinous possibilities, living nature has only chosen one specific compound which is now the universal carrier of hydrogen for absolutely all of the living world. This substance is pyridine nucleotide (DPN), a substance in which two molecules of mononucleotide are united by pyrophosphate bonds, one of the mononucleotides having adenine as its base while the other has nicotinamide. Pyridine nucleotide is to be found as one of the most important biochemical mechanisms in microbes and in higher plants and animals, in heterotrophs and in autotrophs, in organisms which produce and oxidise various sugars in their respiration and in organisms whose sources of carbon are phenol and other related derivatives of hydrocarbons. There can be no doubt that pyridine nucleotide acted as a hydrogen carrier in oxido-reductive reactions even in those distant times when the tree of life was still unbranched, at least as concerns that part of it which was to give rise to the whole living world of the present day.

Nevertheless, it is hardly likely that such a complicated substance as pyridine nucleotide can have been the very first hydrogen carrier. In all probability the earliest evolving organisms used many other far simpler compounds derived from the external medium as hydrogen carriers.

It was from this very primitive basis that the first improvements in living things took place. It was only later, when the conditions necessary for the constant repetition of the synthesis of pyridine nucleotide had been ensured, by means which we shall discuss below, that this compound assumed a monopolistic position in biological metabolism and all the less efficient mechanisms were eliminated irreversibly by natural selection. We do not find them in contemporary organisms so our comparative biochemical lead has not yet plumbed the depths of those times when the very first beginnings of biological metabolism existed, but still, we have approached fairly close to the source of life.

In the simplest case of our flowing system the energy liberated in the course of the oxido-reductive reaction would have been dispersed as heat while the membrane surrounding the system remained unchanged or static. In such a system the reaction and structure are, as it were, independent of one another. In the process of emergence of life, however, these two aspects of the organisation must have become connected with one another. In his detailed study of the fibrillary and membranous systems of various living bodies F. Schmitt reached the conclusion that, although the properties of these systems are determined by the internal structure of the macro-molecules and their ability to aggregate, all of them (including the superficial membrane surrounding the protoplasm) remained lifeless formations until energy was introduced into them from outside. In the case of the original system discussed above, energy could only reach it from outside on account of the oxido-reductive reactions going on inside the system. Thus, from a biological point of view, it is not only the actual possibility of liberating energy in the system that is important, but also the harnessing of the energy which is liberated and its utilisation. This, however, requires special accessory ' harnessing mechanisms ' without which life in general is impossible. " The most fundamental requirement of living matter, which must be met if it is to exist at all," writes M. Dixon in this connection " is that it should contain a mechanism whereby free energy from such chemical reactions as the oxidation of foodstuffs is made available for carrying out energy-requiring reactions and processes instead of being lost as heat." The general idea behind all these mechanisms is that, as a result of a series of transformations of the substance which serves as the original source of energy, compounds containing energy-rich bonds are formed. These bonds will yield about 10,000 cal./mole of free energy on hydrolysis while ordinary hydrolysis of carbohydrates, fats or proteins yields no more than 2-4000 cal./mole. A great variety of organic compounds can possess such high-energy bonds. There are many such substances in living nature having acidic anhydride (acylphosphatic or pyrophosphatic), phosphoamide or thioester bonds. However, in the matter of the transfer of energy in living things adenosine triphosphate (ATP) occupies an absolutely outstanding position. Like pyridine nucleotide, it is to be found in all contemporary organisms without exception. It consists of adenylic mononucleotide united by pyrophosphate bonds with two further molecules of phosphoric acid. These bonds are energy-rich. Thus, if one molecule of phosphoric acid is split off from ATP, adenosine diphosphate (ADP) is formed with the liberation of about 12,000 cal./mole.

An equal amount of energy, given off by the transformation of the original foodstuffs, may be stored in a single energy-rich pyrophosphate bond by using that energy to synthesise ATP from ADP.

Contemporary organisms which can respire, synthesise the greater part of their ATP by means of the energy obtained from the oxidation, by the oxygen of the air, of the hydrogen carried by pyridine nucleotide. This reaction, however, can only take place in the presence of special chemical mechanisms which are possessed only by organisms which are capable of respiration and not by anaerobes. It follows that this cannot be regarded as a primary metabolic pathway (it will be discussed further later).

Alongside this method of formation of ATP there are, however, others which are universal for the whole living world and which form the basis for both aerobic and anaerobic metabolism.

In all of living nature the phosphorylation of ADP is achieved by routes which follow one of three schemes:

1. Anaerobic oxidation of 3-phosphoglyceraldehyde to 3-phosphoglyceric acid:—

   $$3\text{-Phosphoglyceraldehyde} + ADP + H_3PO_4 + DPN \longrightarrow$$
   $$\longrightarrow 3\text{-Phosphoglyceric acid} + ATP + DPN\text{-H}.$$

2. The conversion of 2-phosphoglyceric acid into pyruvic acid:—

   $$2\text{-Phosphoglyceric acid} + ADP \rightarrow \text{Pyruvic acid} + ATP + H_2O.$$

3. The oxidative decarboxylation of α-keto acids which can take place in the presence of oxygen or anaerobically:—

   $$\alpha\text{-Ketoglutaric acid} + ADP + H_3PO_4 + DPN \rightarrow \text{Succinic acid} + ATP + DPN\text{-H} + CO_2.$$

(DPN=pyridine nucleotide, DPN-H=reduced pyridine nucleotide)

Not one of these three reactions is a single chemical act (as it has been represented for simplicity in the equations) but rather a fairly complicated collection of processes following one after another.* One may, however, suppose that these collections of reactions were elaborated comparatively soon

* We may give, as an example, the following chain of chemical events which underlies the first of the schemes. The first stage is the formation of a complex between the aldehyde group of the substrate (3-phosphoglyceraldehyde) and the sulphydryl group of the glutathione-enzyme-protein. This complex gives hydrogen to the pyridine nucleotide. This leads to the formation of an acyl mercaptan, a substance with an energy-rich bond. Phosphorolysis of the acyl mercaptan then takes place and the acyl radical is transferred from its sulphur atom to a phosphate group. 1-3 diphosphoglyceric acid is formed and this has an energy-rich carboxyl phosphate grouping. Finally the phosphate group is transferred from the carboxyl group to the ADP and ATP is formed.

after the origin of life, as we find them as individual links in absolutely all of the metabolic systems which we know now.

The ATP which is formed in these ways is a very widely distributed source of energy for the most varied of vital phenomena requiring free energy such as, for example, the osmotic work involved in absorption and excretion, mechanical work in movement etc. We will return to these phenomena later but must here concentrate our attention on the significance of ATP in those synthetic processes without which the organism could not carry on its continual self-reproduction in the face of its breakdown which is always going on.

The processes which have been most thoroughly studied in this respect are those of the polymerisation which occurs when starch or glycogen is formed from glucose.

They can be represented schematically by the following three reactions occurring successively:—

$$\text{Glucose} + \text{ATP} \rightarrow \text{Glucose 6-phosphate} + \text{ADP}$$
$$\text{Glucose 6-phosphate} \rightarrow \text{Glucose 1-phosphate}$$
$$\text{Glucose 1-phosphate} \rightarrow \text{Glycogen} + H_3PO_4$$

In a similar way the participation of ATP in the synthesis of pyridine nucleotide (DPN) can be represented by the following chain of reactions:—

$$\alpha\text{-Ribose} + \text{ATP} \rightarrow \text{Ribose 5-phosphate} + \text{ADP}$$
$$\text{Ribose 5-phosphate} \rightarrow \text{Ribose 1-phosphate}$$
$$\text{Nicotinamide} + \text{Ribose 1-phosphate} \rightarrow \text{Nicotinamide riboside} + H_3PO_4$$
$$\text{Nicotinamide riboside} + \text{ATP} \rightarrow \text{Nicotinamide mononucleotide} + \text{ADP}$$
$$\text{Nicotinamide mononucleotide} + \text{ATP} \rightarrow \text{DPN} + \text{Pyrophosphate}.$$

According to the recent studies of S. Ochoa, M. Grunberg-Manago, A. Kornberg and others, the process of formation of nucleic acids, like that of polysaccharide formation, may constitute a reversed phosphorolysis, although in this case the major rôle falls to ADP and other diphosphomononucleotides rather than to ATP. ATP certainly plays a part in the biosynthesis of proteins, but the mechanism of this process is still not at all clear.

We are now able to point to a large number of further examples which indicate that ATP is the fundamental source of energy which enables many biosyntheses to take place. In many cases, however, ATP alone is not enough. For purposes of reduction hydrogen carried by DPN is also often required. Furthermore, in all biosyntheses involving the formation of a direct bond between two carbon atoms a third substance is necessary which is as biologically ubiquitous as ATP and DPN. This is the so-called coenzyme A (CoA).

As the work of F. Lipmann, T. Lynen and others has shown, coenzyme A is a fairly complicated compound, the molecule of which contains adenyl mononucleotide, phosphoric acid, pantothenic acid and thioethanolamine. Thus CoA, like ATP and DPN, is a mononucleotide derivative. Its significance was first established in the activation of acetic acid, which occupies a very important position in biological metabolism, being the connecting link between carbohydrates, proteins and fats. In itself, however, acetic acid is metabolically inert; before it can enter into a reaction of acetylation or condensation it must, therefore, be activated in some way. This is done by the formation of acetyl coenzyme A which is a thioester of acetic acid and coenzyme A. The thioester bond formed in this way is energy-rich (8200 cal./mole are liberated by its hydrolysis) so free energy is needed for its synthesis. This may be supplied by ATP, perhaps in accordance with the equations:

$$Acetate + ATP \rightarrow Acetyl\ AMP + Pyrophosphate$$
$$Acetyl\ AMP + CoA \rightarrow Acetyl\ CoA + AMP$$

(AMP=adenosine monophosphoric acid=adenyl mononucleotide).

The acetyl residue which has been activated in this way by coenzyme A can take part in the most varied reactions, e.g. condensation, leading to the formation of new carbon-carbon bonds and the lengthening of the carbon chain such as occurs, for example, when the higher fatty acids are synthesised. Other acids of both the aliphatic and aromatic series can enter into condensation reactions in the same way as acetic acid.

The tremendous biological importance of coenzyme A thus consists in the fact that it mediates the uniting of small organic molecules by means of carbon-carbon bonds to form complicated compounds of high molecular weight; that is to say, it mediates one of the fundamental processes in the synthesis of the carbon skeleton of the components of protoplasm. Some process of this sort must have arisen at a very early stage of biological evolution and the mechanism which is responsible for it (CoA) is therefore to be found throughout the living world.

It is important for the argument later on to note that the presence of coenzyme A also makes it possible for carbon dioxide to enter into combination with the organic substances of living bodies. This so-called heterotrophic fixation of CO_2 occurs in all living things without exception. In the first organisms, however, this was only supplementary to the important synthetic processes and did not play any considerable part in metabolism, for in such fixation there was no increase in the free energy of the organic compounds, on the contrary, there was a loss of such energy. Afterwards, however, as we shall see, this reaction formed an important component of the autotrophic metabolism which developed considerably later.

Thus, three of the chemical mechanisms which we have described (DPN, ATP and CoA) and the limited number of reactions which they could bring about at such an extremely early stage of evolution served as a basis for the transformation of the original colloidal formations into open systems of such a kind that their very existence depended on the constant accomplishment within them of processes of breakdown and synthesis so that the systems were capable of self-preservation and even of growth under conditions where they were continually interacting with the external medium.

Of course, as we have already remarked, systems having these mechanisms can hardly be regarded as the very earliest living things. In these the parts of DPN, ATP and CoA must really have been played by less complicated compounds and the set of different reactions of breakdown and synthesis must have been even simpler than we have represented them above. However, with knowledge in its existing state we cannot enter into the even more ancient period in the development of life which followed immediately on its origin but are forced to try to imagine the history of that development starting from systems which are already endowed with the set of reactions and chemical mechanisms which have been described above.

Two principles formed the foundation of the whole of the further course of evolution. The first concerns the energetic aspect. On the basis of his studies of the thermodynamics of open systems I. Prigogine has reached the conclusion that it is the system in which the increase of entropy is least which must be regarded as the most advanced. He, therefore, considers that in the process of evolution of biological systems their entropy must gradually decrease as they become more complicated and more advanced. Recently T. Matsunoya has put forward an interesting equation in which the dissipation of energy in biological systems serves as a criterion for the degree of advancement of their metabolic organisation. In particular cases this criterion gives results which coincide with those obtained by assessing the advancement of the energetic organisation of the system on the basis of its specific coefficient of useful activity, but the former criterion appears to be considerably more generally applicable.

Matsunoya has shown that, according to the criteria which he has chosen, progressive evolution of metabolism must always tend towards increasing the complexity of the courses of the reactions and increasing the number of links in the chains of reactions.

This principle is also consistent with the second of the principles to which we have referred, which deals with the evolution of the organisation of synthetic processes. The factor which was of the greatest importance for the progressive evolution of the original systems was not the fortuitous acquisition of some particular compound from the external medium, but the appearance in the system of co-ordinated reactions which would ensure the continual synthesis of that compound by the uninterrupted interaction of the system with the external medium.

The great likeness between the composition of the first organisms and that of the surrounding medium was due (as we have already seen) not to the complexity and specificity of the latter, but, on the contrary, to the simplicity of organisation of the first living thing. The less complicated and specific the ingredients of the original biological systems and the more their chemical nature resembled that of the compounds which abounded in the ' primaeval nutrient broth ', the fewer the links required in the chains by which these specific ingredients were synthesised within the system and the more elementary the organisation of the system, but the greater its dependence on the external medium. Naturally, selection of the first organisms was directed towards diminishing this dependence which always threatened the organism with destruction and towards a form of organisation which would ensure the creation of substances which were more and more complicated and specifically adapted to the fulfilment of particular biological functions from the various non-specific substances in the surrounding medium. For this purpose the substances had first to be ' depersonalised ', i.e. broken down into comparatively small and uniform fragments from which any specific ingredient of the system could be built up by standard methods, though these might involve chains of reactions having many links.

In contemporary organisms which have pursued a long road of development one does, in fact, find such a form of organisation of constructive metabolism. In them all, the complicated ingredients of protoplasm are built up from very simple starting substances of low molecular weight such as ammonia, acetic acid, glycine, succinic acid, keto acids etc. These compounds originate as fragments of the organic sources of nourishment derived from the external medium and broken down by destructive metabolism. In contemporary metabolism, therefore, the constructive and destructive sides are closely associated with one another and are only two aspects of a single process.

However, the existence of such a metabolic system requires a very complicated network of reactions with many links, in which an enormous number of chemical events are accurately and steadily co-ordinated in time. The progressive evolution of the original organisms was, in fact, moving towards the development and perfection of such a many-linked network.

The set of reactions essential to all living things, which has been mentioned above, was present in them. While serving as their chemical mechanism in the process of evolution it supplemented itself in many directions and was always elaborating new mechanisms. In present-day organisms, therefore, we only find them as component elements in the general network of metabolism, only individual links, though very important ones, in long chains and cycles of reactions. A comparative study of the organisation of these chains and cycles in various representatives of the living world is very helpful towards an understanding of the development of life at a period of its existence which is now very remote.

Some sort of carbohydrates form the main source of carbon and the basis of the energy metabolism of the great majority of present-day organisms. They may enter the organism from the environment or be synthesised by it. It is hard to say whether this form of metabolism was the actual ' trunk ' of the ' tree of life ' before it had branched or whether it was only an early and important branch.

Studies of the metabolism of several micro-organisms isolated from the soil of petroleum-bearing regions have raised some doubt as to whether the carbohydrates were the sole source of nourishment of the first organisms. These living things cannot assimilate sugar and their only sources of carbon and energy are the hydrocarbons of petroleum and their closest derivatives, for example, paraffins, phenols, toluene, salicylic acid etc. Unfortunately there is no irreproachable evidence which would enable us to say with certainty whether these organisms are the direct descendants of the main trunk of the ' tree of life ' or whether their peculiar form of metabolism has arisen secondarily. In either case it is very suggestive that the essential transfer of hydrogen in oxidoreductive reactions which is common to all the living world and the mechanisms for harnessing energy are found in these organisms too. However that may be, one must suppose that the main branch of the ' tree of life ' which obtained an almost monopolistic position in the process of development, was the carbohydrate branch of metabolism. It is clear that even at the very base of this branch there must have been formed the particular, very complicated set of reactions, that many-linked chain of chemical transformations which we now find in one or other of its closely related variants, as a metabolic feature of almost all present-day organisms.

A diagram of this chain of reactions, which underlies alcoholic and lactic fermentation in microbes, glycolysis in animals and the so-called 'intramolecular respiration' of higher plants is given in fig. 7.

It consists of 12 consecutive essential reactions such that the sequence is the same throughout this long chain for all the processes mentioned above and only at the end of it, when pyruvic acid is formed, does it branch with the formation of lactic acid in lactic fermentation and ethyl alcohol and carbon dioxide in alcoholic fermentation. Among the reactions in this chain we find some which we already know, such as the transformation of 3-phosphoglyceraldehyde into 3-phospho-glyceric acid and 2-phosphoglycerate into pyruvate. The essential mechanisms for the transfer of hydrogen and the 'accumulation' of energy operating here are DPN and ATP, the only thing which has to be added is thiaminepyrophosphate (TPP) which takes part in the decarboxylation of pyruvic acid.

The essential complexity of this chain as compared with the relatively simple sets of reactions which we have discussed above, is connected with its starting point, with the suitable preparation of the substrate (sugar) for the oxido-reductive reactions which form the main source of energy. This preparation consists, on the one hand, in the raising of the energetic level of the sugar molecule by its phosphorylation with the help of ATP and, on the other, in the splitting of the hexose diphosphate produced in this way into two molecules of triose phosphate.

If we bear in mind the criterion for the stage of advancement of metabolic organisation in looking at this increase in complexity, we must admit unreservedly that it is a step forward as compared to the original form of organisation.

This particular, effective sequence of chemical transformations in the fairly complicated chain of fermentative reactions is not achieved by any spatial localisation of the processes, but mainly by organisation in time, by establishing a strictly co-ordinated relationship between the rates of the individual reactions forming links in the chain. Thus, in the organisation of the fermentative series of reactions on its own, the structure

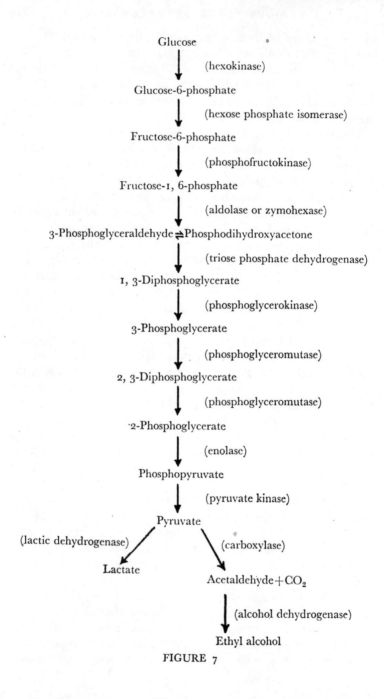

FIGURE 7

of living bodies did not play the extremely important part which falls to it now in realising the more complicated but far more recently developed form of metabolic organisation. The series of intermediate reactions responsible for alcoholic fermentations can be brought about even in a homogenous aqueous solution, of which Buchner's yeast extract was the first example.

It is, however, quite evident that with this form of organisation, the longer the metabolic chain of chemical reactions the more accurately will their rates have to be co-ordinated and the more efficient a mechanism is required for carrying them out. The relatively simple and non-specific catalysts, with which the original forms of living things were provided, were not nearly good enough even for the accurate co-ordination of the rates of the 12 essential reactions of alcoholic fermentation. In the course of evolutionary development these so-called coenzymes (DPN, ATP, CoA etc.) had to be supplemented by substances of a protein nature which were more powerful and more specific in their catalytic activity, namely enzymes.

In the yeast cell, and, therefore, also in Buchner's juice, one can find a whole arsenal of these catalysts each of which specifically increases by many millions or even thousands of millions of times the rate of just one member of the chain of reactions in fermentation. These give rise to a position in which any intermediate product can, for practical purposes, only change in one, strictly determinate direction and the process, therefore, follows a completely determinate track. In the diagram of fermentation given above, the names of the enzymes taking part are given in brackets alongside the arrows which indicate the direction of the reactions which they catalyse.

The specificity of the catalytic action of enzymes is based on a striking spatial correspondence between two or more active atomic groupings. This arrangement is brought about both by the strictly determinate sequence of the amino acid residues in the polypeptide chain and by the regular, spatial architectonic sequence of its folding in the formation of the protein globule.

Sequences and structures of this kind could, of course, not have arisen on their own and therefore the protein-like polymers which formed the basis for the formation of the coacervate droplets can hardly have had the properties which are specific for present-day enzymes.

The amazing correspondence between the intramolecular structure of contemporary enzymes and the biological functions performed by them can only have arisen in the course of natural selection.

We are still a long way from having a full understanding of the process of biosynthesis of protein-enzymes. However, as was stated in the previous chapter, we know that at least three different categories of protoplasmic mechanisms must participate in their formation. These are:—

1. Systems supplying the energy for synthesis.

2. Systems creating the kinetic conditions necessary for it i.e. the particular relationships between the velocities of the different reactions, and, finally,

3. Systems providing for the spatial organisation of the protein globule being formed.

One may suppose that the two first of these categories were already present, although only in a very primitive form, even in the entities from which the whole living world evolved. They alone, however, could not ensure the very precise arrangement of active groups in the protein globule required for enzymic activity. The gradual development and improvement of both intramolecular and multimolecular structures was necessary for this.

One of the most important structural elements in the cellular cytoplasm of contemporary higher organisms is the endoplasmic reticulum. This is a whole system of lipoprotein membranes which forms a very delicate lacework through the rest of the cytoplasm, sometimes called the cytoplasmic matrix (fig. 8).* On the surface of these membranes (which are about 70-150 Å thick) there are granules of ribonucleoprotein 150-200 Å in diameter. Such granules may also be found floating freely in the body of the cytoplasm. Centrifugation has been used successfully by many authors for the isolation of other objects, too, from the cytoplasm of liver cells. These are the microsomes, which are formations with a diameter of

*Figure 8 follows page 52.

500-2000 Å, and which, according to the information in the scientific literature, are foci for the synthesis of proteins (especially enzymic proteins) when they are supplied with activated amino acids (fig. 9).*

Quite recently, however, G. Palade has shown that the microsomes are most probably bubble-like artefacts enclosed in a lipoprotein membrane formed by disruption of the endoplasmic reticulum and bearing ribonucleoprotein granules. Palade considers that the intracytoplasmic membranes of the reticulum must be regarded as superstructures which arose only when living bodies had reached a very high level of development. They are not to be found in the cytoplasm of bacteria and they are evidently not necessary for the organisation and functioning of the simpler types of cell. Palade attributes their appearance in higher organisms to the greater volume of their cells and the lessened surface available for the passage of substances into them as well as to the increased difficulty of diffusion which these caused. At a high level of biological organisation these difficulties are resolved by folding in the external membrane, which then forms a reticulum.

Thus, the most primitive intracytoplasmic stuctural elements seem to be the ribonucleoprotein granules which cannot attain a size greater than 14 protein molecules with an average molecular weight of 35,000. Such granules have been isolated from bacteria also, but they cannot synthesise proteins on their own. It may be that, for this purpose, they have to be associated with a lipoprotein membrane.

We have already noted that such an envelope must have been the first obligatory condition for the formation of any open system which could serve as a starting point for biological evolution. In coacervate droplets which had such membranes, the conditions were far more favourable for the formation of various polymers than in the surrounding medium, if only because " the formation of intermolecular complexes of various types " to use the apposite expression of G. Wald " gives rise to a considerable possibility of counteracting intramolecular disintegration ".

In more highly organised open systems, such as the original, most primitive organisms which have been described above, in which oxido-reductive processes are continually going on

*Figure 9 follows page 52.

and in which the sources of energy (ATP) arose in a place where they were readily accessible for use, the possibilities of developing the synthesis of protein-like and nucleic acid-like polymers were very greatly enlarged. This, naturally, led to a partial removal of complexes of such polymers from the general mass of substances by their precipitation in the form of insoluble formations. This, in its turn, prevented the setting up of an equilibrium between the breakdown and synthesis of polymers, thus favouring synthetic processes.

One may easily imagine that this could have acted as a basis for the formation of nucleoprotein-like granules in the extremely primitive living bodies at a very early stage in the development of life. These granules, perhaps in association with previously existing, lipoprotein surface membranes might, as we have shown, have served as prototypes for the systems which now provide for the synthesis of protein particles with a definite amino acid sequence and three-dimensional arrangement. In this connection an important part is played by the multimolecular organisation of the structure as well as by the intramolecular arrangement of the ribonucleic acid which enters into the composition of the granule. It is not, however, to be supposed that there suddenly appeared in the original systems some molecule of a ribonucleic acid which already had such a highly developed structure that it could, on its own and against the general background of the synthetic processes going on in the system, account for the origin of a protein with a specific structure having exactly such an arrangement of atomic grouping as is characteristic, for example, of the aldolase of yeast or any other particular enzyme. The structure of the very earliest granules themselves and of the molecules of which they were composed was very non-specific, highly variable and poorly adapted to the fulfilment of biological functions. The distribution of the atomic groupings in the protein-like substance which first took part in catalysing the breakdown of hexose diphosphate are as hard to identify with the very precise arrangement of active centres in contemporary aldolase as, for example, the fins of a shark, having a structure adapted only to a primitive form of movement, are to identify with the highly developed arms of a man.

The organisation of the metabolism of the original organisms was hardly what metabolism is now. The reactions forming parts of it were incomparably slower than they are now and the co-ordination between the individual reactions was poor. There were many side-reactions alongside the main line of the vital processes so that much of the nutrient material was frittered away and a large percentage of its energy was dissipated as heat. However, in the process of interaction of the organism with its environment and by the continuous action of natural selection over many hundreds of millions of years, both the living system itself and its individual mechanisms were brought to a higher state of perfection. In particular, the enzyme-proteins and the processes involved in their synthesis became more efficient and better and better adapted to their biological functions.

One must keep it clearly in mind that certainly no less and probably more variants of organisation were tested and rejected in the course of evolution from the original protein-like catalysts to the extremely precisely constructed enzymes than in the development of the human hand.

The majority of these variants have been irrevocably lost to us as their evolution was mainly completed long before the internal organisation of even the most primitive of contemporary living things had come into being. We can, therefore, only isolate enzymes with a very highly developed structure from contemporary organisms. However, proteins having exactly the same enzymic function in different representatives of the living world of to-day differ widely from each other in their chemical natures. The amylase of bacteria is not the same as the amylase of higher plants and the phosphoesterase of leucocytes is quite a different protein from the phosphoesterase of yeast. It may be hoped that, by making a deeper study of this aspect of affairs, we shall be able to investigate the phenomenon of the improvement of enzymes in the course of evolution, although only in its later stages.

At present we can only take note of the very important fact that the number of original, primitive catalysts of living bodies—the coenzymes—was quite insignificant in comparison with the number of catalytic mechanisms which supplement them at a higher stage in the development of living material—the enzymes. It is only the appearance and further development of these latter which has made possible the establishment of long chains of well-co-ordinated metabolic reactions. The system of reactions which, taken as a whole, form the bio-chemical basis of alcoholic or lactic fermentation, clearly arose at a relatively early stage in the evolution of living bodies. This is indicated by their extremely wide distribution and by the fact that they are an obligatory part of the metabolism of the most diverse representatives of the living world. This system must, clearly, be very effective biologically since it was set up in comparatively primitive organisms more than 1,000,000,000 years ago and has persisted throughout the development of living matter, being retained even in the metabolism of the higher plants and animals of the present day. The most widely distributed part of this chain is its earlier part, which is exactly the same throughout the whole of the living world. It is only at the last link that branching occurs, leading to the formation of alcohol and carbon dioxide in plants and lactic acid in animals.

These two types of anaerobic breakdown of carbohydrates formed the main routes in the evolutionary development of destructive metabolism in the principal branches of the ' tree of life '. Of course, many more or less efficient variants must have arisen in the course of their evolution. Many of these must have been completely eradicated by natural selection and have been lost irrevocably, others, on the contrary, have been retained but have come down to us only as comparatively thin shoots which took their origin from the main branches of the ' tree of life '. We can, therefore, now find a large number of different types of anaerobic fermentation but each is confined to a relatively limited group of lower organisms. Even here, in the great majority of cases, the first links of the chain are just the same as those we find in alcoholic or lactic fermentation and it is only after pyruvic acid has been formed that there is a parting of the ways. This certainly suggests that all these fermentations had a common origin, and that they developed from a single common trunk.

Figure 10 shows a diagram of the divergence of the paths of the reactions in different forms of anaerobic fermentation which starts at the pyruvic acid formed by the set of reactions which has been described for alcoholic fermentation on p. 120 (fig. 7).

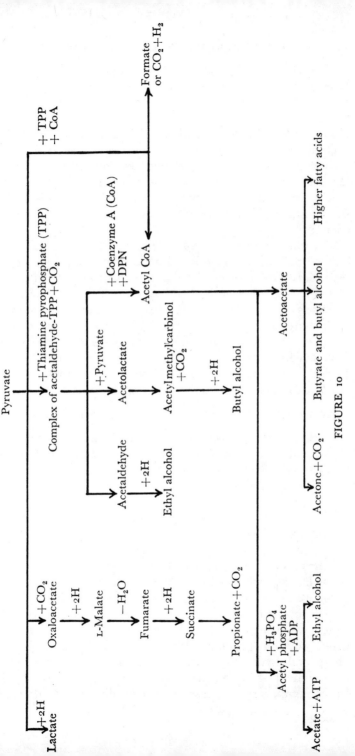

FIGURE 10

Inspection of this diagram shows that, according to what type of fermentation is taking place, products other than ethyl alcohol, carbon dioxide and lactic acid may be formed, in particular, formic, acetic, propionic, succinic, butyric and other higher fatty acids, propyl and butyl alcohols, dimethyl carbinol, acetone and gaseous hydrogen as well as others. It is characteristic that this variety is achieved by the inclusion of a very few 'supplementary' reactions and always by the use of catalytic mechanisms which are very like one another. The whole thing simply amounts to varying the combinations of the same set of chemical events.

Of course, neither alcoholic and lactic fermentation nor any of the other anaerobic fermentations which have been mentioned, are to be regarded as some sort of isolated destructive processes. They are all closely associated with the synthetic reactions of constructive metabolism, supplying the energy and immediate structural materials for them. For example, pyruvic acid, which occupies a key position in all types of fermentation, can easily react with ammonia and hydrogen carried by pyridine nucleotide to form one of the most important amino acids, namely alanine. The equation is as follows:—

$$\text{Pyruvic acid} + \text{Ammonia} + \text{DPN.H}_2 \rightarrow \text{Alanine} + \text{DPN} + \text{H}_2\text{O}$$

Other keto acids behave in the same way. The fragments of molecules which arise as intermediate products of fermentation can condense with one another to form long open chains and closed aromatic or heterocyclic molecules with the help of CoA, etc.

The better the temporal co-ordination of the reactions in a given type of metabolism the less will be the energy dissipated in it and the greater the proportion of the nutrient material which is used for construction of ingredients of the system and, in the last analysis, the more efficient will it be biologically and the more progressive from an evolutionary standpoint.

However, the very closely related metabolic pathways which we have discussed are, of course, not the only ones which would be possible in the presence of the reducing atmosphere and hydrosphere which existed at the period in the development of life on the Earth with which we are dealing. In contemporary organisms we can find other alternative means of transforming organic substances. H. Krebs and H. Kornberg believe that the pentose phosphate cycle is one such means. A diagram of this, taken from their book, is given in fig. 11.

In this cycle, unlike the forms of fermentation which have already been discussed, there is no breakdown of the molecules

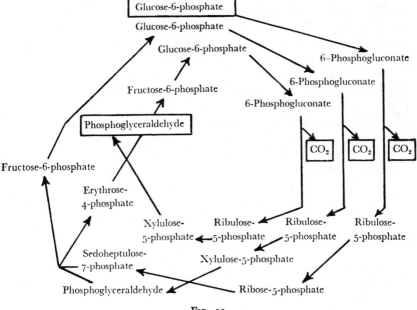

FIG. 11.

of phosphorylated sugar into two molecules of triose phosphate but immediately after its formation the glucose-6-phosphate undergoes anaerobic oxidation and CO_2 is split off from the phosphogluconic acid thus formed, leading to the formation of a phospho-derivative of a pentose. In particular, this pathway is very important in the building of nucleotides and ribose of nucleic acid.

The pentose phosphate cycle is a far less widely distributed form of carbohydrate metabolism than alcoholic or lactic fermentation.

It is only in a few micro-organisms that this cycle is the main method of breakdown of carbohydrates. In the majority it simply supplements the usual forms of fermentation. As has been shown by experiments with radioactively marked glucose, it is only a small part of the sugar which is split by the pentose phosphate cycle and it is clear that its main significance lies in the formation of ribose.

It may be supposed that the pentose phosphate cycle came into being even later than the main types of fermentation. H. Krebs and H. Kornberg write: " It is very probable that the most ancient organisms had no need for it. . . ." Its later origin is indicated by the fact that it includes the fundamental reactions of fermentation alongside some newly developed reactions. Furthermore, for the sake of what will be said later, it is important to note that reactions occur in the pentose phosphate cycle which are of outstanding importance in the process of photosynthesis.*

Many of the forms of metabolism which we have discussed demonstrate the variety of pathways followed by the evolution of organisms even in the absence of free oxygen in the surrounding medium, but in the presence of ready-made organic substances, i.e. under anaerobic, heterotrophic conditions.

The reserves of organic materials contained in the ' world nutrient broth ' were being replenished all the time by means of abiogenic synthetic reactions, but this process was relatively slow and, as life developed, so it became more and more inadequate to meet the nutritional requirements of the primaeval living things. As a result of this, the stocks must have been depleted and, if the development of life had only proceeded along the lines we have discussed, they would, sooner or later, have disappeared completely.

Some contemporary authors believe that this would have happened very quickly, in the course of some thousands of years. Their calculations are, however, based on an obvious misapprehension. Of couse, if the primaeval ' world broth ' could, in some way, have been seeded with contemporary micro-organisms which were able to multiply in it without hindrance to an unlimited extent, then, if you like, thousands of years would have been plenty of time for the complete destruction of the stores of organic substances. However, one must

---

* Some authors, unlike Krebs and Kornberg, even consider that the pentose phosphate cycle may have only arisen at the same time as photosynthesis or perhaps even later.

not forget that the prodigiously fast tempo of the vital processes of contemporary organisms is the result of an improvement of metabolism which has been going on for 2,000,000,000 years. In the first organisms, however, the reactions proceeded many millions of times less quickly than do the enzymic transformations which we know. It was not until organisms had achieved a considerable level of efficiency through evolution they they were faced by any real threat of a shortage of those organic substances which were their only available sources of nourishment.

This caused an extreme aggravation of the struggle for existence and was a powerful factor in the further evolution of the primaeval organisms. In the process of their development they began to set up more and more new systems which enabled them, not merely to make more rational use of exogenous organic substances, but also to use other and simpler carbon compounds as nutrients as well as using sources of free energy which were more widely available in the external medium.

PHOTOCHEMICAL REACTIONS

Solar radiation is the most powerful and inexhaustible source of energy on the surface of the Earth. As we have already seen, the main photochemical activities on the Earth before the appearance of life were brought about by short-wave ultraviolet radiations. The development of life, however, proceeded by using long-wave radiations, which are obviously more readily available to organisms.

It has long been established that the energy of visible light can be used to bring about oxido-reductive processes in the presence of organic pigments which can absorb the light. According to A. Terenin, when a molecule of the pigment absorbs light it enters the ' biradical ' state and acquires a high chemical reactivity which enables the radicals to take up or give off an electron or a hydrogen ion and thus to accomplish oxido-reductive processes which could not have come about on their own, in the dark, without the addition of energy in the form of light.

Porphyrins could act the part of such pigments in organisms. These compounds must have made their appearance among the components of living bodies at a rather early stage in their development. In this respect they are, perhaps, comparable with the coenzymes pyridine nucleotide and thiamine pyrophosphate already discussed. Compounds of porphyrins with iron are very widely distributed in the living world to-day, a well-known example being the red pigment of our blood called haemin.

In animals which respire, compounds of iron with porphyrins play a very important part in oxidative reactions in which free oxygen takes part. However, these compounds arose in living bodies long before large amounts of free oxygen appeared in the atmosphere of the Earth. Thus, they may be found even in typical anaerobes such as *Desulfovibrio desulfuricans.*

All these processes can take place satisfactorily in the dark, for no use is as yet being made of an important property of porphyrins which is associated with their colour, that is to say, with their ability to absorb light.

However, unlike iron-porphyrin compounds, free porphyrins and, especially, complexes of porphyrins with magnesium, which have no ordinary catalytic power in the dark, can have photocatalytic effects. The mechanism by which iron-porphyrin compounds take part in biologically important catalytic processes is based on the reversible oxido-reduction of the central iron atom which takes place in the dark. The works of A. Krasnovskiï and his colleagues have shown that complexes of porphyrins with magnesium, namely bacterio-chlorophyll and the chlorophyll of higher plants, as well as free porphyrins without any metal, such as haematoporphyrin, can undergo reversible reduction (by taking up an electron or hydrogen) only when they absorb an appropriate quantum of light. When this happens there is a photocatalytic transfer of an electron or hydrogen, which is to be distinguished from catalytic processes such as can occur in the dark. This leads to a raising of the energy level of the products of the photo-reaction. Part of the energy absorbed is, as it were, ' put into storage ' in a very mobile and easily used form.

In the earliest period of the existence of life, when there was an abundance of primary organic compounds in the external medium, light may not have been of decisive importance to organisms as a source of energy. However, as the ready-made organic substances began to disappear, and as they became increasingly deficient in the surrounding solution, a greater and greater advantage in the struggle for life was enjoyed by those organisms which were in a position to use their porphyrins, not only to catalyse reactions occurring in the dark, but also as photocatalysts. They thus acquired the ability to use light as a supplementary source of energy. The first thing which this did was to enable the earliest coloured organisms to make a radical rationalisation of their heterotrophic metabolism and to use exogenous organic substances in it far more efficiently without undergoing any significant redesigning of their previously existing organisation.

Ordinary heterotrophs were forced to convert a large percentage of the organic substances which they had obtained from the external medium into waste products which they could not use any more, such as alcohol, organic acids etc. The earliest coloured organisms, on the other hand, used the ' gratuitous ' energy of light to metabolise them and this freed them from the need to dissipate exogenous organic substances irrationally. This was the original purpose of photochemical reactions, not the primary synthesis of organic substances.

We can see this from a study of the metabolism of contemporary pigmented bacteria, in particular the Athiorhodaceae. From an external point of view, that is to say, when one considers the overall balance, the metabolism of these bacteria is of the ordinary heterotrophic type. In the light they can develop freely under anaerobic conditions on solutions which must contain organic substances (e.g. butyric acid or other equivalent compounds). As the mass of the bacterial growth increases, so the amount of exogenous organic material in the surrounding medium decreases correspondingly and, at the same time, the bacteria give off a small amount of carbon dioxide into the atmosphere.

Their internal biochemical mechanisms are, however, considerably more complicated. Like other organisms which possess CoA, they can fix the carbon dioxide of the atmosphere. But, by using the increased energy of the pigments after they have absorbed light, bacteria of the Athiorhodaceae bring about a photocatalytic transfer of hydrogen, reducing the carbon dioxide and oxidising the exogenous organic substances. They, therefore, do not have to make unusable waste products as other heterotrophs must and, in the light, Athiorhodaceae use organic substances almost completely (90 per cent. or more) for the building up of their own mass while in ordinary heterotrophs (those not using light) unusable waste products account for the lion's share of the nutrient material.

Other pigmented bacteria carry out their metabolism in the same way as the Athiorhodaceae but, in them, the source (donor) of hydrogen for the reduction of carbon dioxide is not organic substances but hydrogen sulphide. This has been demonstrated by the very interesting studies of C. van Niel on the purple and green sulphur bacteria (Thiorhodaceae) living in shallow bays and lagoons of sea water which are rich in hydrogen sulphide and well illuminated by the sun.

All these primitive pigmented organisms have mechanisms of a kind which will enable them to carry out the reversible photochemical transfer of an electron or hydrogen at the expense of absorbed light, but as their original sources of hydrogen they can only use the most easily available reducing substances such as organic compounds, hydrogen sulphide, molecular hydrogen etc.

The process of progressive evolution of photosynthetic organisms was directed towards enabling them to use a far wider group of substances as hydrogen donors.

This path of development inevitably ended in photosynthetic reactions involving the most ' difficult ' but also the most ' ubiquitous ' hydrogen donor, namely, water. The oxygen of the water was then liberated in molecular form.

Some contemporary organisms are interesting in that they retain metabolic features of a more primitive organisation of photosynthetic processes, but the ability to give off molecular oxygen usually characterises even them. They are, as it were, intermediate links between the first photosynthetic organisms and the highly organised photoautotrophs.

One particular such organism is the green alga *Scenedesmus* which has had its metabolism studied in detail in this connection by H. Gaffron.

PHOTOSYNTHESIS

There can be no doubt, however, that the trunk road of development of autotrophy was photosynthesis in the form in which we now see it in the higher plants. The use of water as a hydrogen donor by photosynthesising organisms was a tremendous step forward on the path of development of biochemical systems, which joined the photostage of the process to cycles of reactions leading to the reduction of carbon dioxide by stages and the formation of molecular oxygen.

This, however, required the prolonged evolution of organisms which were already fairly highly developed and which possessed a large arsenal of different metabolic mechanisms. A knowledge of the photosynthetic apparatus of modern plants convinces us that this must be so. It is extremely complicated and has still been by no means fully worked out in spite of many studies.

To make the position clearer we will indulge in an analogy which is, of course, as they always must be, very rough. Let us take, as our example of a complicated machine performing a definite job, the engine of a car. The work of the engine depends, not only on its main component, the cylinder block, but also on a number of auxiliary mechanisms including some which comprise whole systems each having its specific task, the preparation and delivery of the combustion mixture, the production of a current with a high voltage to ignite the mixture, cooling, lubrication, the transmission of motion, regulation of speed etc.

If the engine is to run smoothly, not only must each of these systems function properly but, even more important, they must be properly co-ordinated in space and time. The spark from the sparking plug must occur when the piston is in a particular position in the cylinder, the mixture must be introduced at a particular moment etc.

Similarly, in the photosynthesising apparatus of plants, there is not just a single chain of chemical transformations, but a number of cycles of biochemical reactions, whole aggregates of catalytic and photochemical systems. It is only when they are very well co-ordinated with one another and interact continually that the desired effect can be obtained. This is achieved, not only by means of a strictly determined set of individual reactions co-ordinated in time, but also by their spatial localisation, the presence of particular structures in the photosynthetic apparatus.

The need for such spatial organisation became particularly acute in connection with the use of water as a hydrogen donor, and with the liberation of oxygen which this entailed. In a process of this sort, it is only by the dispersal of the original unstable products of photosynthesis into heterogeneous structures that the reaction can be prevented from following the thermodynamically more probable, reverse path. In pigmented bacteria which photosynthesise under anaerobic conditions without forming free oxygen, the pigments are distributed diffusely through the protoplasm. The higher form of photosynthesis, on the other hand, only became possible when the process of evolution of organisms had led to the formation of special, complicated structural apparatuses.

In higher plants the chloroplasts act as such an apparatus. Nobody has yet succeeded in reproducing the process of photosynthesis entirely in any homogeneous mixtures from which chloroplasts were absent, unlike the position in alcoholic fermentation. This in itself indicates the importance of the part played by spatial organisation in photosynthesis.

Study of the plastids with the electron microscope has shown that they are complicated structures consisting of a colourless stroma on which are scattered chlorophyll-containing granules in the form of flat cylinders (fig. 12).* The granules consist of discs of protein combined with a layer of chlorophyll-containing lipid. Thus, in the chlorophyll granule we find the same ' sandwich ' type of structure as in the surface membrane of all living bodies or the endoplasmic reticulum of more highly organised living creatures. In the chloroplast, however, this structure has been converted into an aggregate which is very highly specialised for carrying out photosynthesis.

It is only in such a lipoprotein structure that the first chemical event in photosynthesis, the splitting of water, can take place. If photosynthesis is to occur, however, this event must be harmoniously linked with a whole series of other processes, each of which is carried out by its own specific enzymic mechanism, ' assembled ' in complete systems or aggregates.

Using, for the most part, the results obtained by M. Calvin, we shall now give a highly simplified diagram of the work of these aggregates, each of which may be characterised by the

*Figure 12 follows page 52.

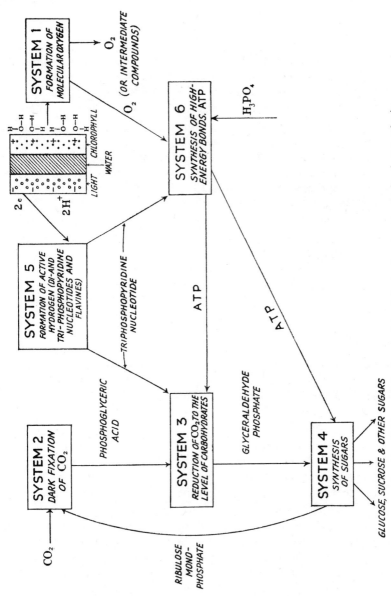

Fig. 13. Scheme of the interaction of the various aggregates in photosynthesis.

functions which it performs in the general process of photosynthesis.

1. The formation of molecular oxygen. 2. The fixation of CO_2 in the dark. 3. The reduction of CO_2 to the level of a carbohydrate. 4. The synthesis of sugars from phosphotrioses. 5. The production of 'active hydrogen' in the form of reduced pyridine nucleotide (DPN-H or TPN-H) (TPN is a substance having a structure similar to that of DPN but containing three, instead of two, phosphate groups per molecule). 6. The formation of high-energy bonds (ATP). *Cf.* fig. 13.

As Calvin puts it figuratively, light falling on the chlorophyll-bearing layer of the lipoprotein aggregate dislodges electrons from it and these are immediately insulated on the structure from the small positive ' holes ' which they left behind. The electrons go towards the reduction of pyridine nucleotide (in system 5) while the positive charges act on water and bring about its oxidation (in system 1), the reaction giving rise to intermediate products in the form of hydrogen peroxide or organic peroxides which are broken down with the formation of molecular oxygen. The oxygen is, for the most part, given off into the atmosphere, but some of it is used in system 6 for processes of oxidative phosphorylation.

On the other hand (in system 2) there is dark fixation of CO_2 which is carried out in essentially the same way and by means of the same mechanisms (e.g. CoA) as in all other living things. Phosphoglyceric acid is obtained by means of the processes occurring in system 2 and is later transformed, in systems 3 and 4, into various sugars. In system 3 it is reduced to triose phosphate (glyceraldehyde). This, however, requires, in the first place ' active hydrogen ' which is supplied in the form of reduced pyridine nucleotide (TPN-H) from system 5 and, in the second place, a readily available source of energy (ATP) which is worked up in system 6.

The further working up of triose phosphates goes on in system 4. It ends, either with their simple condensation to form first hexose diphosphates and then glucose, or with more complicated transformations which lead to the appearance of phosphoric esters of all the monosaccharides characteristic of the vegetable kingdom, having four, five, six, seven or ten carbon atoms. A substance of particular importance formed here is the phosphoric ester of the pentose ribulose, a substance which, as we have already seen, is a characteristic intermediate product of the pentose phosphate cycle of fermentation. Ribulose monophosphate plays a very important part in photosynthesis as, after further phosphorylation at the expense of ATP, it passes into system 2 where it acts as a primary acceptor of CO_2 in the process of its dark fixation.

A detailed acquaintance with the photosynthetic apparatus of green plants shows that all these catalytic mechanisms, and even whole aggregates of them, are not by any means new in principle. In most cases we find the same, or similar, mechanisms in colourless organisms or in the photosynthetic bacteria.

Thus these chemical mechanisms existed even before the appearance of green plants on the Earth and before the development of modern forms of photosynthesis, but they were dispersed and not properly combined to form a single complicated system. It was, in fact, this union of previously existing mechanisms which occurred when the photosynthetic apparatus came into being. It could only be formed in the process of the evolution of organisms on the basis of previously existing systems and aggregates. To carry our analogy with the engine of a car further, we may say that, as the history of technology shows, it could only arise on the basis of previously existing apparatus. Before the invention of the steam piston and cylinder or the dynamo etc. such an engine could not have been built no matter how great a genius had tried.

The appearance of photosynthesis represented an extremely important stage in the process of evolution of the organic world of our planet. It made a radical change in all previously existing relationships.

With the appearance of free oxygen even previously existing colourless organisms acquired essentially new possibilities for a decisive rationalisation of their metabolism, which did not involve any radical change in their old mechanisms. For example, the transition of some obligate anaerobes to facultative aerobiosis can readily be imagined to have happened by the alteration of only one link in their metabolism, the change from anaerobic to oxidative decarboxylation of pyruvic acid.

By doing this, such facultative anaerobes as *Escherichia coli* and *Streptococcus faecalis* can, under aerobic conditions, not merely break sugar down to lactic acid, but they can also oxidise it to acetic acid which, from the energetic point of view, is considerably more favourable. In the absence of free oxygen the formation of acetic acid must inevitably be accompanied by the formation of some reduced product such as ethyl alcohol which, under such conditions, is an unusable waste product for these organisms. The acetic acid bacteria, on the other hand, which are more confirmed aerobes, not only convert sugar to acetic acid, they also convert ethyl alcohol to acetic acid, thus including it once more in energy metabolism and mobilising the energy of this waste product of fermentation which had previously been quite unusable by heterotrophs.

The evolutionary line which arose in this way gave rise to the appearance of the many different facultative aerobes which carry on so-called oxidative fermentations.

It was, I believe, in this transitional epoch that the metabolism of such peculiar groups of organisms as the chemoautotrophs also appeared. It was just at the dividing line between reducing and oxidising conditions that the widest variety of fundamentally different possibilities of using molecular oxygen to oxidise the reduced compounds of the crust of the Earth were created.

At the period we are discussing, when free oxygen was beginning to be formed, these oxidative reactions must have been going on at, literally, every point on the surface of the Earth, for substrates which could be oxidised were present everywhere. However, these reactions were abiogenic and took place comparatively slowly and the energy which was released by them was dissipated in the form of heat.

Under conditions where there was an acute shortage of organic, exogenous compounds those organisms, which were able to include in their evolutionary development these reactions of oxidation of inorganic substances and which formed, in their bodies, catalytic mechanisms to accelerate these processes and to mobilise their energy for synthetic purposes, naturally enjoyed a great advantage in the struggle for existence and were therefore strengthened by natural selection and later became widely distributed.

As is to be expected, the forms of life capable of autotrophy which we find nowadays are organisms which, under natural conditions, live in the very places where the reduced substances of the depths of the Earth come out into the light of day on the surface and encounter the molecular oxygen of the atmosphere.

The part played by chemoautotrophs in the circulation of material at the present time is therefore very important. Practically all naturally occurring processes of oxidation of reduced compounds of nitrogen and sulphur, as well as hydrogen and methane and, to some extent, iron, are associated with the vital activities of the appropriate micro-organisms.

The great systematic diversity of the groups of chemoautotrophs and the closeness of some of them to various of the metabolically more primitive heterotrophs, which are joined to some by transitional forms of organism, convinces one that chemoautotrophy did not just arise once but that the beginning of its luxuriant development must be referred to the time when there already existed a great variety of organic forms.

The specific conditions of the period under discussion which promoted this development were, in the first place, a shortage of organic nutrients with a large store of inorganic sources of energy. However, as conditions on the surface of the Earth became oxidative this store diminished quickly and was only replenished comparatively slowly from the deeper layers of the crust of the Earth. The balance of organic substances in the biosphere, on the contrary, was becoming more and more favourable owing to the appearance and rapid development of the photoautotrophs.

This allowed the main current of evolution to return to its old channel in the further development of organisms which were adapted to the assimilation of organic substances. The period of acute shortage of these substances began to pass over and there only remained, as a biological reminder, a small group of autotrophic organisms capable of chemosynthesis. These only constituted a lateral branch of the main stream of evolution. This main channel now comprised the green plants—photoautotrophs—and colourless organisms, in particular animals, which retained their former, more ancient faculty for heterotrophic feeding. After the origin of photosynthesis, however, the evolution of even those organisms which used ready-made organic substances in their vital processes began to have a quite different biochemical form from what it had before this event.

The decisive factor in this respect was the oxygen in the atmosphere, the presence of which permitted considerable rationalisation and intensification of the process of mobilisation of the energy of organic substances. This rationalisation was, of course, based on the same anaerobic mechanisms which had formed the foundation of the energy metabolism of the early heterotrophs.

However, the organisms which were preserved and strengthened by natural selection in the process of evolution under the new aerobic conditions were those which had developed auxiliary enzymic complexes and systems of reactions which enabled them to obtain from their exogenous organic substances far more high-energy bonds than they could previously, by oxidising these substances completely by means of the oxygen of the air.

Two new systems were required to carry out this task: in the first place a system for mobilisation of the hydrogen which would have been wasted under anaerobic conditions, being excreted by the organism in the form of more or less useless compounds (such as acids, alcohols etc.) or even in the form of gaseous hydrogen; in the second place, a system for the activation of oxygen whereby hydrogen could be oxidised to water. The individual mechanisms of the first system are very ancient. In essence they were present even in anaerobic organisms. They are the DNP, ATP, CoA etc. which are already well known to us. Only their action in aerobiosis has been extended to give a number of new products which are not present in the chain of alcoholic or lactic fermentation. In itself this chain of primary transformation of carbohydrate has been kept unchanged even in aerobes, but in them new chains and cycles have been linked to it at particular points. The individual reactions of these chains and cycles transfer hydrogen to pyridine nucleotide or other such acceptors (e.g. flavine derivatives).

The sites at which these cycles are linked on are exactly

determined even in fairly primitive facultative anaerobes. The most important site is pyruvic acid, the key point from which the pathways of the various forms of anaerobic fermentation radiated in different directions. As we have already indicated in the case of *Streptococcus faecalis*, pyruvic acid may be converted into acetic acid by oxidative decarboxylation. In the bacteria responsible for propionic fermentation the reverse process occurs, pyruvic acid combines with CO_2 and forms oxaloacetic acid. In higher organisms which are capable of respiration, both of these processes of transformation are carried out on pyruvic acid which has been made in the usual way. This, however, is not the end of the matter. There has arisen a closed chain of transformations with many links which has been called the Krebs cycle or the di- and tricarboxylic acid cycle. A diagram of it is given in fig. 14.

For the sake of simplicity the diagram omits the course of the anaerobic transformation of glucose into pyruvic acid which is common to all the organisms.

We shall not deal in detail with all the links in this complicated cycle, in which many of the mechanisms such as CoA, which we have already met, play their part but we must note the following points.

In the course of this cycle all three of the carbon atoms of pyruvic acid are oxidised to CO_2 at the expense of the oxygen of water, while the water is simultaneously drawn into the cycle with the help of pyridine nucleotides and the corresponding enzymes called dehydrogenases. The direct splitting off of CO_2 is brought about by carboxylases, which are enzymes containing thiamine pyrophosphate (TPP). Thus we see that the same categories of enzymic mechanisms operate here as in anaerobic metabolism but the sequence of the reactions is substantially changed. The main difference is that the hydrogen which is liberated is not wasted but is used to acquire a significant extra quantity of energy by its oxidation by the oxygen of the air. The intermediate products which arise during the cycle link it with other metabolic systems and this results in the establishment of a direct link and mutual dependence between the metabolism of carbohydrates, fats, organic acids and proteins. To take a particular example: the keto acids which arise in the course of the cycle can either be

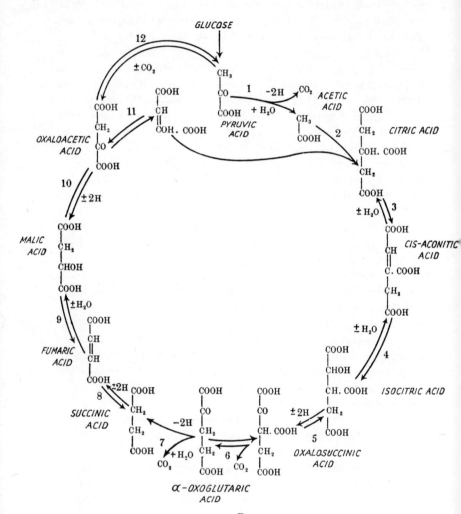

Fig. 14.

aminated directly by reacting with ammonia, or can be converted by transamination into alanine or glutamic or aspartic acid and these can be used for the formation of the other amino acids which take part in the synthesis of proteins, hormones, enzymes etc.

The linking of the accessory respiratory transformations with the chain of fermentation reactions can occur, not only through the pyruvic acid at the end of the chain, but also through its first link. In this case respiration is linked with the pentose phosphate cycle, which assumes its aerobic form, for the most part, in contemporary organisms.

The removal of hydrogen from the intermediate products of the Krebs cycle by pyridine nucleotide is not associated with the giving off of any appreciable amount of energy. The free energy of oxidation becomes available, not on the oxidation of the substrate but on the subsequent oxidation of the reduced form of pyridine nucleotide by the oxygen of the air. This, however, does not occur as a single event but by the transfer of protons and electrons along the chain of a series of special oxidative enzymes. As a result of this transfer, each of the intermediate carriers, which are only present in very small amounts, is reduced at the expense of the substrate and is oxidised by the oxygen of the air. This sort of oxidation is accompanied by phosphorylation and is generally known as oxidative phosphorylation. It is a very considerable, not to say essential, source of free energy for aerobic organisms. In fact, it has recently been shown that the oxidation of only one molecule of reduced pyridine nucleotide provides for the formation of three phosphate bonds while the fermentation of a whole molecule of sugar only provides for the synthesis of two such high-energy bonds.

Quite a variety of substances (mediators) can serve as intermediate links in the oxidative chain in different organisms, but the flavoproteins hold pride of place. As G. Mahler has shown recently, one can find a great variety of compounds of this type among the different representatives of the living world. In some of these the flavine group may be united with nucleotides and other organic residues and also with such metals as iron, molybdenum or copper.

In individual cases the flavoprotein enzymes, having

obtained hydrogen from reduced pyridine nucleotide, pass it on to porphyrins, which are components of the cytochrome system or perhaps to other intermediate oxidative mechanisms which can bring about the final oxidation of this hydrogen by the oxygen of the air. Other cases involve the participation of flavoproteins which are capable of obtaining hydrogen directly from the substrate and transferring it to the cytochrome system. Finally, there are some flavoproteins which can transfer the hydrogen which they procure directly to molecular oxygen.

The great variety of the sequences of reactions in the oxidative chains in the different representatives of the animal and vegetable kingdoms is, itself, an indication of the relative youth of this system for, in the process of evolution, it developed in parallel in different organisms at the very stage of the development of the animate world when there occurred a profound differentiation between its separate parts.

An acquaintance with the various enzymes taking part in the oxidative transformations in various organisms must also lead one to the same conclusion. This is especially true of the ' terminal group ' of such catalysts as directly activate molecular oxygen. In organisms which are widely separated systematically this effect is often achieved by widely differing catalytic mechanisms. Alongside the most ancient flavine enzymes one must mention first and foremost the cytochromes, which have been found even in fairly primitive anaerobes.

With the appearance of molecular oxygen in the atmosphere of the Earth, the most widely differing representatives of the living world could easily use their cytochromes as oxidative mechanisms by adapting them to the activation of oxygen in the process of respiration.

In this connection the cytochromes and their associated enzymes, the cytochrome oxidases, seem to be very widely distributed as respiratory aggregates; we find them in groups of organisms of very different systematic origins, but their importance is specially great in the respiratory process of many micro-organisms as well as in the animal cell. In higher plants the phenol oxidase system plays the main part in this respect. In this system the enzymes are cuproproteins and the hydrogen carriers the ' respiratory chromogens ' of Palladin. These mechanisms are very specific for plants. It is clear that, in the process of phylogenesis, these had already been elaborated at the time when organisms became separated into the animal and vegetable kingdoms.

In the respiration of plants, peroxidase is very important in activating the oxygen of hydrogen peroxide, whereas in the animal cell it plays a comparatively small part.

The terminal oxidation by the oxygen of the air may be catalysed by ascorbic oxidase, lipoxidase and numbers of other mechanisms as well as by cytochrome oxidase, phenol oxidase, peroxidase and flavine derivatives.

In different sorts of living things and at different stages in their life cycles the parts played by these different mechanisms may vary within very wide limits. This all suggests that the process of respiration is, phylogenetically, very recent and that it came into being considerably later than the anaerobic method of energy metabolism.

THE EVOLUTION OF CELLULAR STRUCTURE

A similar conclusion must be drawn from the great complexity of spatial organisation of the protoplasm needed for carrying out respiration. While fermentation and the anaerobic phosphorylation associated with it can be carried out in homogeneous solutions, the mechanisms of respiration and oxidative phosphorylation are closely bound up with specific structures of living bodies. Attempts to carry out these processes simply in a solution of the appropriate enzymes and mediators have always ended in failure. It is clear that protons and electrons can only be passed along the chain of the oxidative systems when these are correctly localised in relation to one another, otherwise the chain will be broken at some point. In this respect the link between the actual oxidation and the phosphorylation is most vulnerable. For example, if the particular concentrations of the specific ingredients are altered, respiration proper may continue but it is irremediably ' uncoupled ' from phosphorylation.

The need for a particular spatial organisation for carrying out respiration is even exhibited by such bacteria as are capable of aerobiosis although they have a considerably simpler protoplasmic structure than have higher organisms. As we have already shown, the essential elements are the lipoprotein cell-membrane (cytoplasmic membrane) and the ribonucleoprotein granules having a diameter of 150-200 Å. In intact bacteria these elements are integrated in some way to form a single system. If the bacteria are lysed with lysozyme while subjected to a high osmotic pressure in the external medium one can obtain so-called protoplasts, in which the spatial organisation has not been destroyed. They can therefore carry on respiration, phosphorylation and synthesis of proteins, especially enzymes. If, however, the osmotic pressure of the surrounding medium is gradually lowered, one can cause a more thorough lysis of the protoplasts and separate the granules from the cytoplasmic membranes, sometimes called " ghosts ". When this happens, the isolated structural elements retain a considerable amount of their enzymic activity and can even bring about particular parts of the respiratory process, such as oxidative phosphorylation (though with a very low coefficient of efficiency) or separate parts of the Krebs cycle, but the process of respiration as a whole and the syntheses associated with it seem to be destroyed and cannot be reproduced even when the systems which have been separated in this way are put together again and allowed to act in concert.

In higher organisms the spatial organisation of respiration has achieved an even greater complexity and efficiency. Here there have arisen, in the process of evolution, structures which are specially adapted for this purpose, namely the mitochondria, which seem to be absent from bacteria (fig. 15). The mitochondria are very small, elongated, flattened bodies which are just visible with the optical microscope and which have been isolated in a number of cases from cells, without destroying their structure or their biochemical functions. When this has been done it has been possible to recognise both the individual, fundamental oxido-reductive enzymes and also whole systems of enzymes required to accomplish the Krebs cycle and to fix and transform energy.

Furthermore, there is some indication that the activation of substrates for biosynthetic processes occurs in the mitochondria, especially the activation of amino acids.

The wide range of biochemical activity of the mitochondria is paralleled by a great intricacy of internal structure, as

*Figure 15 follows page 52.

revealed by electron microscopy especially when using ultra-fine sections. In particular, it shows a very highly developed system of lipoprotein membranous structures which seem to be the most striking and generally found forms of spatial organisation in living bodies.

The lipoprotein membranes form an outer surface envelope enclosing the whole mitochondrion and a system of internal compartments, the number and arrangement of which is very variable. These internal membranes are immersed in a basic material which appears to be finely granular and in which one can often see specialised components. In most mammalian cells the membranes are arranged parallel to one another and perpendicularly to the long axes of the mitochondria. They are rather closely packed. Thanks to the strictly determinate arrangement of the enzymic complexes on the ultra-fine structure of the mitochondria, an extremely high level of functional efficiency is attained by the apparatus as a whole. A particular example is the high efficiency of the process of transfer of electrons in the system of flavoprotein and haem enzymes in the mitochondria. D. Green ascribes this to contact being made between the groups of enzymes by the lipoprotein membranes.

Thus, the mitochondria of contemporary higher organisms, like the chloroplasts of plants, are very complicated and highly developed structures, well adapted to the fulfilment of particular biological functions. It is clear that such apparatus could only have arisen during the course of prolonged development of living things, by increasing the efficiency of their aerobic metabolism, long after oxygen had appeared on a large scale in the atmosphere of the Earth. This is suggested by the fact that the structure of the mitochondria can only exist when there is a comparatively high partial pressure of oxygen. As P. Govodan and his colleagues have shown, mitochondria become vacuolated and destroyed if the oxygen content of the surrounding medium falls to less than 30 per cent. of its ordinary level.

Unfortunately we have not yet got enough facts to enable us to reconstruct the pathway by which mitochondria were formed from more primitive protoplasmic structures in the process of the evolutionary development of organisms.

This is even more true in regard to that other important

intracellular structure, the nucleus. The facts to be found in the literature concerning the formation of this structure in the process of the evolution of living matter are extremely scanty. One therefore often meets with preconceived ideas in this field, which are by no means axiomatic but are seriously lacking any scientific foundations. It seems to me that the belief that desoxyribonucleic acid, which is one of the most important components of the nucleus, appeared at the very moment of the origin of life and was, in fact, the ' first living molecule ', is one such preconceived idea.

This idea is very widely held and may be said to be the current opinion in contemporary biological literature. It has been transcribed without any substantial change from paper to paper and from book to book. However, the only fact which those expressing the idea bring forward to justify their belief is its invariable presence in all living things.

As we have already seen, DNA holds no monopoly of this universality. This ubiquitous distribution is also found with many other compounds, particularly the coenzymes DPN, ATP, CoA etc., and also in respect of whole complexes of molecules such as the lipoprotein surface membranes. Furthermore, even the complicated chain of reactions of alcoholic or lactic fermentation, especially its earlier links, are also invariable properties of all existing organisms. Nevertheless we cannot assume that this complicated combination of strictly co-ordinated reactions arose at the very source of life and did not require the prolonged evolution of the original living things for its formation.

As we have already seen, from some of the large amount of evidence which we have discussed, the first thing which these systems required was an envelope to separate the system from the external medium and after that they needed mechanisms to enable them to carry out oxido-reductive reactions and to mobilise the energy thus obtained for synthetic purposes. This formed the basis for the development of the powers of self-preservation and self-reproduction in the organism which, even if it was still very primitive, was based on the continual repetition of a particular set of reactions.

However, not even the later and more highly developed metabolic mechanisms such as DPN, ATP and CoA, let alone the very earliest ones, were very closely related, chemically, to DNA. Not one of them contained the reduced form of ribose which is a specific component of DNA.

When the increasing complexity and efficiency of the metabolic mechanisms required the very precise co-ordination in time of many of the individual reactions in the chains of fermentation and synthesis, the protein enzymes came into being. For their effective action they needed very great accuracy of arrangement of active atomic groups, that is to say, particular intramolecular architectonics of the protein globule. In this connection mechanisms were needed which would be able to regulate the final organisation of the non-specific polymers of amino acids, which were being synthesised in the system, and thus ensure the appearance of proteins which, even at this stage, were adapted to the fulfilment of their enzymic functions.

However, the important part in the performance of this task again did not fall to DNA, but fell to RNA, as will be clear to anyone who is familiar with bacterial ribonucleic granules and is demonstrated by experiments in which viral ribonucleic acid is introduced into the living cell of the tobacco plant. This compound alters the course of the synthesis of proteins and nucleic acids normally occurring in the plant and, by regulating the final configuration of the products obtained, leads to the constant reiteration of the formation of strictly determinate polymers which are foreign to the plant, against a background of the plant's own synthetic processes.

Only many, many millions of years after the origin of life, when the complexity of the organisation of living bodies had increased greatly and when the problem of the more or less accurate self-reproduction of this organisation, therefore, could not be solved satisfactorily by a single reaction constantly taking place within the system, did there arise the necessity for creating a new mechanism which would guarantee the essential conservatism of the living system. DNA, with its great metabolic inertia, was such a mechanism. Thus, one may suppose that the appearance of DNA only became necessary when the development of living bodies had already reached a comparatively high level.

This idea was put forward very colourfully by Lindegren

in the form of the following analogy. He writes that electrical communications are, of course, absolutely necessary for a large town like Chicago, but this does not mean that no town could have existed or developed earlier without such communications. Similarly, DNA is necessary to the extremely highly organised living things which now exist. This necessity, however, derives from the high complexity of their organisation. As we have already seen, more primitive organisms could develop and accomplish the whole of their lifetime while using, for this purpose, mechanisms which did not include DNA. The necessity for this compound only arose in connection with the difficulties and contradictions which came into being as the very labile and dynamic form of organisation of living bodies was elaborated. The origin of DNA should, therefore, not be thought of as happening at the moment of the appearance of life on the Earth, but should be looked for at a fairly high stage in the development of the organic world, at the base of the evolutionary branch of the ' tree of life ' from which the highly organised living things, which have come down to our times, took their origin.

I know that this exposition of my ideas will seem heretical to many orthodox geneticists and they may regard me as anathema on that account, but an unbiassed analysis of all that I have said in this chapter about the earliest period in the development of life has caused me to believe that the conclusions I have drawn are inescapable.

Of course, the intramolecular structure of DNA, like that of proteins and RNA, must have evolved over a long period and become better and better adapted to its function of passing on hereditary traits. However, the multimolecular structures which were formed from DNA must have played a very important part in this connection. This must have been specially important in ensuring the equal distribution of DNA in cell division. We find this spatial organisation at a relatively low level of development in bacteria and blue-green algae. In them, unlike more highly organised cells, the nuclear material is simply arranged in the centre of the protoplast in the form of spherical or twisted bodies composed of DNA and having the chemical properties characteristic of the nucleus. These bodies, however, do not correspond structurally with the typical nucleus of the cell of a higher organism, in that they lack the internal structural differentiation characteristic of these latter and are not separated from the cytoplasm around them by a visible membrane. When the cells of bacteria and blue-green algae divide there is probably a simple division of nuclear material between the two daughter cells.

The part played by the internal structure of the nucleus became far greater with the appearance of the conjugation of cells and especially in connection with the sexual process. When this had emerged the problem of the proper distribution of nuclear material became immeasurably more complicated. This led to the formation of a new and amazingly delicate and precise organisation of the nucleus, which now became capable of mitosis. This organisation could, naturally, only have been elaborated in the process of a further very prolonged evolution of organisms which had already reached a fairly high stage of development.

Thus, at the end of this chapter we reach the conclusion that the emergence of the cell in its contemporary form, that cell which we usually regard as the very earliest and indispensable element of life, required at least a half of the whole time during which life has existed on the Earth.

CHAPTER IV

THE FURTHER EVOLUTION OF LIFE

Nunc ea quae sentire videmus cumque necessest
Ex insensilibus tamen omnia confiteare
Principiis constare.

LUCRETIUS—*De rerum natura.**

GENERAL TRENDS IN THE FURTHER EVOLUTION OF LIFE

W E have now surveyed the detailed internal structures
and complicated metabolic systems of living bodies,
the ways in which they are organised both in time
and in space, which developed during the first half of the
period for which life has existed on the Earth, and have proved
to be so satisfactory in the course of further evolution that
there has been no radical change in them in the whole of the
later development of life. They have only been supplemented
in various ways and have been retained until our own time as
the common and indispensable form of organisation for all
living things, in spite of the fact that the world of living
things has evolved at a tremendous rate, giving rise to an
endless variety of microbes, plants and animals.

There are some particular properties, found in all living
things, which are associated with these forms of organisation
and are a direct consequence of them. First there is the
ability to absorb substances selectively from the surrounding
medium and to excrete the products of metabolism back into
that medium. Then there is the power of growth, multiplication, self-reproduction, dispersal in space and, finally, the
responsive reaction of organisms to external influences which
is so characteristic of everything living, its irritability.

All of these properties are to be found, to a greater or less
extent, in any living thing known to us to-day and, taken
together, they differentiate organisms qualitatively from objects
of the inorganic world. It is therefore to be understood that

---

* At this stage you must admit that whatever is seen to be sentient is nevertheless composed of atoms that are insentient.   Trans. R. E. Latham.

a detailed acquaintance with these properties is absolutely necessary for an understanding of the essential nature of life. Our acquaintance with them is, however, far from being complete enough for us to understand fully this essential nature.

The earliest period of biological evolution, which we have already surveyed, is only a part of the general ' line of life ' which was mentioned in the first chapter of this book. The development of life certainly was not completed at the end of this period, on the contrary, it continued at a greater and greater speed and in the later stages it was not flowing in a single channel but was developing along widely ramifying paths. Along these evolutionary paths there arose new qualities which had been absent in the earliest period of the development of life and which are now not present in the whole of the living world, but which we cannot ignore if we are to get a true and complete picture of life.

It is obviously quite impossible to undertake a detailed and complete examination of all these qualities in this book. It is not even necessary to do so, as such an examination has already been made in a number of specialised works. Here we shall only dwell on general tendencies in the further evolution of life and note the sequence and essential mode of development of these qualities.

PROGRESSIVE STRENGTHENING OF UNITY OF ORGANISM AND ENVIRONMENT

In the first chapter of this book we directed our attention to the clearly observable, specific interaction between the organism and its environment which may be described as their dialectical unity and which runs, like a red thread, through the whole development of life on the Earth. The strengthening of this unity and the establishment of new links between the organism and more and more distant regions of the external world, and, alongside this, the creation of a situation in which the organism was able to exist under an ever wider range of external conditions, represented and still represent the fundamental tendency of biological evolution, both in the earliest period, which we have already surveyed, and in all the succeeding periods of the development of life.

The progressive strengthening and extension of these

links between the organism and its environment can, however, only be accomplished by their continually being particularised and differentiated.

It is, of course, true that every primitive object of the inorganic world, such as a single grain of sand in the desert, is also linked to the whole world around it. It gravitates, not only towards the neighbouring grains of sand, but also towards the planets, the Sun and the more distant stars and cosmic bodies. This linkage is, however, generalised and not particularised and this makes it less intimate. A far more highly differentiated and, therefore, more highly developed linkage is that between a microbe and the nutrient broth around it from which it selectively acquires the substances it needs and into which it discharges the products of its metabolism. However, even these links, which are considerably more highly differentiated than those of the inorganic world, are still essentially confined to the very limited region of space in immediate contact with the microbe.

As the development of life proceeded, so the linkages between the organism and the external world were strengthened and extended till, on the basis of far-reaching differentiation, they attained the very high degree of organisation seen only in very highly developed living things.

" Imagine to yourself" wrote the well-known Russian physicist N. Umov at the beginning of this century, " 5,000,000,000 beads scattered over the surface of the globe. They are as small in relation to it as are the small grains of sand to the desert. Let us suppose that each of these beads has, drawn upon it, a miniature map of the sky with the millions of stars which light it. Let us further suppose that each bead responds, not just to one constellation on this map, but that it directs its axis to first one point in the sky and then to another. This tiny globe distinguishes things at an immeasurably great distance from itself. This is no fantasy or eastern fairy tale. These beads are the eyes of men scattered over the face of the Earth ".

Thus, there can be no doubt that the general direction of progressive evolution is towards the strengthening of the bonds between the organism and the world around it, manifesting itself in the increasing particularisation and differentiation of these bonds. Such differentiation can, however, only be attained if there is a continual increase in the complexity of the living systems. In fact, if we study the history of the development of life by tracing the transition from lower to higher forms, we shall soon be convinced that the material progress of life consists in the ever increasing complexity of living bodies, an increase in complexity which is associated with differentiation of the parts of the organism, with their specialisation and is directed towards the fulfilment of particular functions by the living system as a whole and the establishment of more bonds between it and its environment.

We have already encountered such differentiation, even in unicellular organisms where it takes the form of the appearance first of primitive and, later, of more highly developed and complicated organelles. This differentiation reaches the highest stage of development within the confines of a single cell in the infusoria, where one finds, in addition to the nucleus and the ordinary organelles, specific feeding and excretory vacuoles, locomotor cilia etc.

DIFFERENTIATION AND ORGANISATION

The possibilities for the development of this sort of differentiation in unicellular organisms were, however, narrowly limited. It could only be substantially extended if the specialisation involved complete cells joined together to form a system rather than simply separate parts of the protoplasm of one cell. A primitive example of such a living system at the cellular level of organisation is provided by sponges. Unlike the infusoria and other protozoa, in which a single cell carries out all the vital functions, we already find in the sponges a division of labour between particular cells which are specialised for the performance of particular functions such as feeding, support and multiplication. In the sponges there is, thus, cellular differentiation but there is still no, or almost no, cellular co-ordination leading to the formation of tissues.

We find such co-ordination in living things which have reached the higher level of tissue organisation, the simplest example being that of the coelenterates. Although there is still a certain division of labour as between cells in this case, these cells are already co-ordinated and combined into more or less uniform tissues which are really responsible for carrying out particular functions.

The next stage of development is the organ level of organisation, exemplified by those living things which possess differentiated organs, i.e. functional units consisting of two or more different types of tissue. The flatworms may serve as the simplest example of organisms of this kind. At the even higher, so-called systematic level of organisation, we find the combination of several organs co-operating with one another to form separate functional systems. In the last analysis this is the way by which the greater and greater efficiency and extent of the co-ordination of all the functional systems of an individual multicellular organism has been achieved.

With the transition to each higher stage of organisation the integration of the organism and its environment increases but, at the same time, there arise difficulties which can only be overcome by a further increase in complexity of the living system. We have already seen this in our examination of the first steps in the evolutionary development of the most primitive organisms which were still engaged in the formation of an intracellular organisation. For example, an increase in the number of links in the metabolic chain, while decreasing the dissipation of energy by living systems, also created greater difficulties in the accurate co-ordination of the reactions. Such co-ordination could only be attained by the emergence of improved protein catalysts, i.e. enzymes, with their high specificity. The inevitable increase in volume, associated with the increase in complexity of living organisms, upset the relationship between that volume and the surface through which the organism could interact with the surrounding medium. This must have hindered the access of substances to the system and also their excretion. In order to overcome this difficulty there had to be a folding of the surface membrane and the formation of an endoplasmic reticulum. Such processes as photosynthesis and respiration demanded accurate spatial organisation of their individual links and this was achieved in the course of evolution by the formation of plastids and mitochondria.

The need to solve the problem of the accurate self-reproduction of living systems under conditions of ever increasing

complexity of their running organisation led to the development
of the new stabilising mechanisms of the cell nucleus.

This applies even more forcibly to the subsequent elaboration of multicellular systems. When once the individual cells
of such a system became differentiated for specialised purposes
this gave rise to an urgent need for the transfer of substances
between cells. This problem was solved by the emergence of
an intercellular medium and, later, by the formation of special
conducting mechanisms along which substances could be
transported far more quickly than by their passing on from
cell to cell. Thus, the greater the size and the more complicated
the structure of the organism, the greater was the need for such
transport.

In the higher plants this was the basis of the formation of
the conducting pathways of xylem and phloem, in animals, of
the blood-circulatory and lymphatic systems. The flow of
blood and lymph in which the cells are bathed forms the
internal environment of the organism, and nutritive substances
from the outside world enter it indirectly, after having undergone preliminary preparation in a special digestive system.
Furthermore, this internal environment is supplied with oxygen
from the lungs and from it the end products of disintegration
are discharged by special excretory systems.

Of course the process of digestion could be carried out
even by unicellular organisms, as, for example, by infusoria
in their digestive vacuoles. It was, however, only the development of the whole digestive system of multicellular animals,
including a number of specialised enzyme-producing glands
and other complicated organs, which made possible the process
of working up of nutrient substances which is necessary for the
differentiated intake of food and which enables the higher
organisms to survive far greater changes in external conditions
than would be possible for unicellular living things.

A further step forward on the road towards this sort of
emancipation of the organism from the external conditions
was the appearance of the precisely controlled constancy of
the internal environment which we find in warm-blooded
animals. In their internal environment, not only is the
temperature maintained at a constant level regardless of
external conditions, but there is also a strictly standardised

level of acidity, oxygen and carbon dioxide concentration, sugar and amino acid content, ratio between phosphate and calcium etc. This enables warm-blooded animals to exist under a very wide range of external conditions. It does, however, require the creation of new and extremely complicated regulatory systems in which the main parts are played by the nervous system and the endocrine glands. In these systems special receptor mechanisms register each deviation from the normal and transmit the appropriate signal by a very complicated pathway to the organ which will restore the disturbed equilibrium.

It is hardly necessary to point out that such far-reaching elaboration of living systems leads to the development of qualitatively new properties which had not existed in the earlier and more primitive organisms.

However, in using a single word to cover qualitatively different properties and phenomena we are often inclined to ignore the differences, and this is hardly conducive to understanding the objects we are studying. For example, we use the single term ' multiplication ' to mean the increase in the number of neutrons in a nuclear reaction, the multiplication of bacteria by simple fission and the increase in numbers of a human population by birth. There is, however, a qualitative difference in principle between these phenomena. Of course, the division of bacterial cells, unlike the simple atomic reaction, is not an elementary act of disintegration. It is a very complicated chain of events which result first in growth of the living system and then in its division in such a way that the separate parts retain their previous organisation both of structure and metabolism.

Similarly, the multiplication of human beings differs from the multiplication of bacteria. With the exception of the origin of Eve from the rib of Adam, as described in the Bible, we know of no case in which a person has reproduced himself vegetatively by simple division of the adult organism.

The production of a new person requires a sexual process, the fusion of two gametes to form a zygote, i.e. the fertilisation of an ovum. This is followed by a complicated process of ontogenetic development of this ovum. At particular stages in this development there are qualitative shifts in metabolism, these shifts being of a different kind in the different cells which have arisen by fission. This leads to an ever increasing differentiation of cells, tissues and organs, like that which occurred in the gradual increase in complexity of organisms in the process of phylogenetic development. It is quite clear that in bacteria there is no such process, nor can there be, as the whole of this development arises out of the later elaboration of multicellular organisms.

However, just as the fundamental properties of all living things, which we enumerated above, are derived directly from their metabolism and their original structure, so the new properties which arise in the process of evolution can be derived from these fundamental properties. It therefore seems to us most rational to consider the later process of evolution of the living world in accordance with the following scheme, provisional though it is.

We must begin by examining each of the fundamental properties of all living things as listed above. We will then try to characterise the qualities which have arisen out of them in the process of evolution and which are only present in organisms of a higher stage of development.

ABSORPTION AND EXCRETION

Let us first examine the ability of living bodies to absorb substances selectively from their environment and to excrete the products of their metabolism back into it. The study of this ability, which underlies the interaction of the organism with its environment and is therefore of the highest importance for an understanding of life, has already been going on intensively for nearly a hundred years. One would have thought that, by now, this property of living bodies which looks, at first sight, so comparatively simple, must have been studied to completion. However, this is not so. Even now the problem of so-called ' cellular permeability ' is still far from being solved. Contrary opinions about it have been expressed and bitter quarrels rage around it.

One of the main reasons for this state of affairs seems to me to be the fact that very little attention is, at present, paid to the evolutionary aspect of the problem which is absolutely essential for a correct solution of it. It is often forgotten that in our investigations we are not dealing with the living cell in general, but with particular biological objects at different levels of evolutionary development. Obviously such neglect of the principle of evolution must lead to a number of misunderstandings and contradictions.

People used to try, and sometimes still try, to explain the ability of living bodies to absorb and discharge substances selectively in terms of the ordinary physico-chemical laws of diffusion and osmosis on the basis of inorganic models of one sort or another. Such an approach can be held to be justifiable, to some extent, in work on the individual colloidal systems which existed before life and from which it was derived. However, even when dealing with the most primitive organisms in this way one must proceed with very great caution for, with the origin of life, there arose new laws of metabolism and biological structure which later determined the whole process of improvement of the metabolism and functions of the early living bodies, especially the selective absorption of substances from the surrounding medium.

It is even more important to bear this factor in mind when working with the highly differentiated cells of higher plants or the muscle and nerve cells of animals or other such biological objects which have come down to us by a long path of evolutionary development. In the course of this development a substantial increase in complexity and, in many cases, a qualitative change, has affected those forms of organisation and metabolism which were characteristic of the first living things. One can therefore hardly hope for success in any attempt mechanically to reduce all these phenomena to the common denominator of elementary physical and chemical processes.

Such an attempt was made even in the sixties of last century. In essence it was an attempt to explain the ability of living things to absorb and discharge selectively purely on the basis of the more or less constant structural properties of the surface membrane of the cell, which envelopes the protoplasm and thus lies on the boundary separating the living body from the environment. The theory built up on this basis was called the membrane theory of cellular permeability. It has retained its dominant position in the scientific literature right up to the present time though, since the moment of its inception, it has undergone many substantial alterations. In its original form the membrane theory might have been formulated briefly as follows: If a cell is immersed in a solution of a substance which is not present within it or, if present, is in a lower concentration inside the cell than in the surrounding medium then, owing to the concentration gradient, this substance will diffuse into the cell. The surface membrane of the cell lies in the way of the diffusion and, according to its internal stucture, it may either hinder this diffusion or bar the way completely, thus promoting a selective flow of substances into and out of the cell.

A film of copper ferrocyanide obtained by M. Traube served as the original model of such a semi-permeable membrane. It only allowed water to pass through it and kept back all the substances dissolved in the water. It was therefore used by W. Pfeffer for the construction of his osmometer, with the help of which he tried to solve the problems of the intake of water and the nourishment of plants via their roots. The results obtained in this way were, however, far more valuable towards establishing the general physico-chemical laws of diffusion of dissolved substances formulated by van't Hoff than towards solving biological problems.

It was, of course, clear *a priori* that other substances must enter the cell from the environment besides water. In biological studies, therefore, more extensive use was made of so-called ' selectively ' permeable membranes which allowed the passage, to a greater or lesser extent, of substances necessary to the cell if dissolved in water. In particular cellophane, collodion sacs and other similar films served as such artificial membranes in many of the model experiments. Their permeability depended on the size of the pores in them. They thus acted like a sieve, letting through substances of low molecular weight but keeping back the large molecules which could not pass through the pores.

Similar considerations were applied to the permeability of such natural ' films ' as the intestinal wall, the scales of onions etc. However, the falsity of such a simple analogy soon became evident. It was shown that, in a number of cases, it was not so much the size of the molecule that was important in determining whether it could penetrate into the cell, as the so-called coefficient of distribution, i.e. the ratio of the solubility of the particular substance in lipids to its solubility in water. The more soluble the substance in question was in lipids the more easily it entered the cell.

This fact was naturally related to the involvement of lipids in the structure of the cell membrane which, as we have already seen, is like a sandwich of protein and lipid layers. However, in order to explain the easy entry of water and some substances dissolved in it into the cell it was necessary to imagine a greater complexity of the structure of the cell membrane by postulating a mosaic structure for it. It was assumed that hydrophobic substances passed into the cell by becoming dissolved in the lipid cell membrane while water-soluble compounds entered it through the hydrophilic pores which penetrated the membrane.

All the same, even such a membrane theory could not give an adequate explanation of many phenomena which had been observed, and many modern authors (e.g. D. Sabinin, D. Nasonov, A. Troshin and others) have therefore denied that it is the structure of the cell membrane which, in itself, is the decisive factor affecting the ability of living bodies to absorb or discharge any particular substance. These authors consider that this ability is a manifestation of the phase properties of the protoplasm as a whole and that it can only be understood with reference to the coacervate nature of protoplasm.

In considering the question of the entry of substances into the cell, they therefore do not put the main emphasis on the ability of the cell membrane to pass any particular substance through itself, but rather on the ability of the protoplasm to absorb these substances from the surrounding medium, that is, on its sorptional properties which may be expressed as the partition coefficient between the protoplasm and the surrounding medium.

Troshin has obtained curves for the distribution of different substances between artificially obtained coacervate droplets and their equilibrium mixtures and has shown that these curves are very like the distribution curves for these substances between living protoplasm and the surrounding solution.

Thus, even the original simple coacervate droplets, which we have already accepted as being the precursors of living bodies, must have been able to absorb substances selectively from the surrounding medium somewhat as protoplasm does now. Such an analogy, of course, remained valid even when these droplets acquired lipoprotein membranes like those obtained by Bungenberg de Jong. However, there was an inescapable and fundamental difference between these objects, which existed before the origin of life, and the first organisms, for the former were 'static' while the latter were 'stationary' systems. In experiments on the entry of substances into artificial coacervate droplets made in the ordinary way, a definite diffusional equilibrium between the droplets and the surrounding solution is always set up quite quickly.

The living body, on the other hand, can never attain such an equilibrium. A cell which is in complete equilibrium with the substances dissolved in the medium is a dead cell. Therefore any question concerning living bodies, especially one concerning their ability to absorb and discharge substances selectively, can only be answered in the light of an understanding of the metabolism which is going on in them.

We have shown already that the first step on the way to the formation of living systems was the appearance of reactions in accordance with the following scheme:

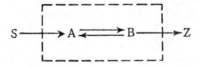

In this case the amount of substance A present in the system but derived from the external medium depends, not only on the rate of its entry into the system, but also on the rate of its transformation into B. The concentration of substance A in the system may be extremely low, not because this substance enters slowly from the external medium, but because it disappears more quickly in the reaction $A \rightarrow B$.

Such a system can therefore extract from the external medium substances which are present there in negligibly small amounts, if such substances enter into one of the reactions characteristic of the system but, on the other hand, even if the concentration of a substance in the outside medium is high it will only enter to a very limited extent if it does not take part in the chemical transformations going on within the system.

Similarly, the rate of formation of *B* plays a decisive part in determining the course of its excretion.

Thus, even at the very earliest stages of the development of metabolism, its effects made a fundamental change in the nature of the processes of absorption and excretion distinguishing them from those which took place in static coacervate drops or their surface films.

This is true even if we only take account of such processes as occur in strict accordance with the gradient of concentration, i.e. when a substance only enters a living system if its concentration is higher in the surrounding medium than in the system and *vice versa*.

ACTIVE TRANSPORT

It is, however, a characteristic feature of living things that movement of substances occurs at a great rate in them, not only in the direction of the gradient of concentration but mainly against it. For example, potassium is usually concentrated in the cells of plants and animals to such an extent that its concentration in them is many times greater than in the surrounding medium. It is self-evident that such a concentration cannot be the result of a simple process of diffusion in which the part played by the protoplasm or its surface membrane amounts to no more than providing a greater or less impediment to this diffusion.

When substances move against the gradient of concentration, diffusion is not the force which moves them. The cell itself participates actively in the process, carrying out a definite amount of work and, therefore, also using up a definite amount of energy, which can only be provided by biological metabolism.

In fact, by using vital stains such as phenolic dyes, we can, in many cases, easily observe directly that the cell actively absorbs the dye from the external medium against the concentration gradient. This, however, only takes place when the cell is carrying out its normal vital activities. If the metabolism is disturbed or suspended in some way, then the active entry of the dye also ceases at once. Furthermore, if the cell is damaged by some poison after it has accumulated the dye, this will be returned to the external medium along the gradient of concentration, for the dead cell is subject only to the ordinary law of diffusion.

It is clearly quite impossible to explain the phenomena peculiar to living bodies altogether in terms of this law. We can only do so by studying the stages of the formation of metabolism. The ability to absorb substances actively (against the gradient of concentration) from the external medium and to excrete them back would seem to have arisen at a comparatively early stage in the formation of living systems, at the time when they developed co-ordinating mechanisms by means of which the free energy of chemical reactions was not dissipated as heat, but became available for processes which needed an access of energy, and, in particular, was transformed into ATP and other compounds with high-energy bonds.

We still have not any reliable evidence to enable us to understand the ways in which this flow of energy, which arose in the process of biological metabolism, might have affected the rate and direction of the active absorption or excretion of substances even at the comparatively primitive stage of development of life which we have been discussing. We can only assume that the accession of energy in a usable form to the cell membrane must have created a profound disturbance of the static character of the membrane (and, indeed, of the whole living body). There began to be constant, often rhythmically repeated, alterations in both the internal structure of the macromolecules of which the membrane was made and of the ways in which they were aggregated. This could lead to a certain rhythm in the absorption of substances from the external medium by the surface of the living body and in their transport within that body.

Thus, what is known as the power of active transfer of substances seems to be at the very basis of the organisation of everything living. It characterises all contemporary organisms. In this connection it is interesting to note that, even in contemporary higher organisms which have the ability to respire aerobically, the impairment or prevention of such respiration does not always suppress the process of active transfer. It may be supposed that, in such cases, the energy required for the transfer is supplied by anaerobic metabolism which, as we saw in the last chapter, arose at a relatively early stage in the development of life. From what has been said it becomes clear that a true understanding of the process of active absorption and excretion can only be achieved by means of a profound understanding of the way in which the process arose in the course of the evolution of metabolism. Unfortunately the schemes of the biological mechanisms of active transfer which are now being put forward in the scientific literature are of a very speculative nature and there is not one which meets with complete, general recognition, just because they take very little account of metabolism and none at all of its evolutionary development.

As an example we may cite just one such scheme of the work of the cell membrane, which has recently been given by D. Miller in his theory of the osmotic pump. According to Miller, the proteins of the gel, of which the membrane is formed, rhythmically increase and decrease their hydrophilia under the influence of enzymes. When they do this they either suck in or squeeze out absorbed water. This leads to the movement of water and substances dissolved in it along channels which pass through the membrane. In such an osmotic pump the part of the valves is played by the molecular groups of the gel which can actively adsorb the dissolved substances. If their ability to hold on to the substances remains unchanged both during hydration and during dehydration of the gel, the process will be passive and the flow will be in the direction of the gradient. If the dissolved substances can only be held by the adsorptive groups when the gel is in one particular state, then there will be active transfer and the flow may be against the gradient of concentration. In spite of the extreme ingenuity of such a scheme and the considerable amount of detail covered by it, it still lacks what is most important, it does not indicate the way in which the work of all the postulated mechanisms is directly associated with metabolism. A reference to some enzyme of the membrane does not help much in this connection. For a proper understanding of the mechanisms of active transfer of substances, one requires an accurate knowledge of which of the particular links in metabolism is associated with each of the phenomena playing a part in the active transfer, and how this in its turn affects the state of the whole metabolic network of reactions. We are here concerned, not with metabolism in general, but with the actual form of metabolism characteristic of the object being studied, for, as metabolism becomes more highly developed and cellular structure more complicated, so the power of active transfer must, inevitably, have altered, acquiring qualitatively new organisational peculiarities.

Unfortunately we still know too little about this evolution to be able to plot its course systematically and to take note of the qualitative shifts in the organisation of active transfer which occurred at particular stages in the development of the living world.

Here we need only remark that the advent of multi-cellularity brought with it a specially great increase in the complexity of the task of active transfer. It brought about the need for a flow of substances right through cells instead of only a flow within an individual cell, a flow which would ensure the quick and effective transfer of compounds of various kinds from one cell to another or even through a whole system of cells and intercellular pathways over quite long distances. We may take as a superficially very simple example of the transport of substances through cells, a phenomenon which occurs in embryonic nephric tubules isolated from a chicken embryo. In the free state these tubules take the form of hollow globules, the internal cavity being separated from the external medium by a continuous layer of cells. Substances from the external medium (such as dyes) can, however, accumulate in the cavity, sometimes in concentrations considerably exceeding those in the external medium. These substances are actively transferred into the cavity through the layer of cells surrounding it which do not themselves contain any significant amount of dye.

All attempts to explain this very simple-seeming phenomenon by means of various, sometimes quite complicated physicochemical mechanisms and schemes are extremely naive and unconvincing. This is quite understandable, as it is not possible to solve this problem by the direct application of the laws of inorganic nature, thus ignoring the evolutionary path of development of the living material. In fact, the phenomenon of the transfer of substances across a cell could only have developed as a result of the orderly development of a historically earlier process of active transfer which, in its turn, grew up on the basis of the development of metabolism which is common to all living things.

In the further evolution of living things the transfer of substances across cells acquired a more and more complex character determined by biological factors. Naturally the systems and phenomena which arose in this way became less and less susceptible to direct mechanical explanation in terms of the elementary processes of inorganic nature. We may here take as our example the translocation of water and substances dissolved in it with the help of root pressure along the vessels of higher plants and the so-called phenomenon of imbibition in animals. This latter term is generally used to mean the process by which various substances pass through a layer of cells into the blood. The most important physiological instance of imbibition is that which occurs in the intestine with the help of specifically organised formations known as villi. In these, the active translocation of substances obtained in the process of digestion is complicated by a large number of accessory phenomena, in particular the repeated rhythmic contractions of the villi, as well as the precise regulation of the process as a whole.

Even in unicellular creatures one can see substantial differences in their ability to absorb and excrete substances under the influence of stimuli of one sort and another so that stimulated and resting cells differ markedly in respect of their ability to translocate substances actively.

In multicellular organisms this feature becomes more and more important in connection with the regulation of absorption, excretion and the translocation of substances in different kinds of tissues and organs.

In the intestinal villi the process of imbibition is regulated, not only by the effects of various chemical compounds, but also by the action of the nervous system. Among the higher members of the animal kingdom it has been shown that even the cortex of the brain plays a regulating part in this process. In particular, it has been shown that the process of imbibition of substances from the intestinal villi into the blood behaves as though it were a conditioned reflex.

The processes of secretion have been found to behave in the same way. For instance, the rate of secretion of digestive enzymes by the appropriate glands of the gastro-intestinal tract is regulated by many reflexes, both unconditioned and conditioned.

NUTRITION

The process of digestion, the process of imbibition and many other associated processes together constitute the process of nutrition in higher animals and man. This process is obviously not merely utterly unlike the simple entry of substances into any individual inorganic system, it also differs fundamentally from the assimilation of substances by microbes from the nutrient broth in which they are floating. It is only with many reservations that we can use the same word for the ' nutrition ' of microbes and the ' nutrition ' of human beings. In essence we have here two phenomena situated at qualitatively different levels of development.

Thus we may picture a successive set of phenomena getting more and more complicated in the course of the evolution of life: 1, elementary absorption of substances from the external medium by living systems which is nevertheless associated with primitive metabolism; 2, active translocation of substances (associated with the expenditure of energy) underlying the absorption and discharge of substances by living cells; 3, active translocation of substances through a system of cells in multicellular organisms; 4, imbibition of substances into the blood of animals and; finally 5, the complicated phenomenon of nutrition in higher animals.

The first member of this series derives its origin directly from the beginnings of metabolism. Each successive member, however, must be considered as resulting from an increase in complexity in the preceding organisation and studied as a particular evolutionary stage in the development of living matter. As history shows us, attempts to skip over all these stages have never led to any good.

We have intentionally dwelt in some detail on the examination of this first essential property of living material and on its subsequent development because the conclusions at which we have arrived, on the basis of our examination, can be extended to cover all the rest of the fundamental properties of all living things which we have enumerated above, their powers of growth, multiplication, self-reproduction, locomotion and dispersal and, finally, irritability. In their most primitive form all of these can be directly derived from metabolism. They come into being and develop concurrently with the increasing elaboration and efficiency of metabolism. However, in the further evolution of living things each of these properties forms the basis for the creation of a set of qualitatively new phenomena, which only occur in higher and higher forms of life. Each of these phenomena can, thus, only be understood in the light of a knowledge of their derivation from the simpler forms of organisation of living material which preceded them.

GROWTH AND DEVELOPMENT

The second of the fundamental properties of living things which we listed above—their power of growth—the irreversible increase in mass associated with the carrying out of their vital activities, occurring at the expense of the substances in the environment—was, in its most primitive form, directly derived from the circumstance that organisms are open systems. In closed systems equilibrium is maintained by an equality between the forward and backward rates of reactions so that in them there cannot, by definition, be any increase in weight. In open systems, on the other hand, the rate of reaction in one direction is regularly greater than that in the other.

However, in the process of selection of the original individual colloidal system in the waters of the primaeval ocean, the only ones which were preserved for future development were those in which the co-ordination of the reactions, which together made up their metabolism, was always directed in such a way that synthesis predominated over breakdown and this must necessarily have led to an increase in mass.

Thus, the power of growth must have been inherent even in the systems from which life originated. When life came into being in the first organisms, this power persisted, only becoming a more orderly and, therefore, more stable characteristic.   In living things chains and cycles of reactions, integrated into a metabolic network, are constantly repeated in time leading to the steady formation of synthetic products and, therefore, to a certain constancy in the composition and structure of the systems which are becoming larger within themselves in spite of the constant flow of ever changing substances through them.   This constancy is, however, only relative.   In the process of their evolutionary elaboration, the original property of living things—their power of growth— was constantly brought into association with the qualitative shifts in metabolism which formed the basis of the ontogenetic development of the organisms.   As this went on, the higher the organism mounted on the scale of evolution the more complicated became its ontogenesis, which is intimately bound up with its growth.   If growth leads only to a quantitative increase in size of the living system, then development is the more profound qualitative differentiation of its parts which arise at particular stages in the individual existence of a given system.

Metabolism, being a network of processes, strictly co-ordinated in time, can, of course, never remain completely unchanging.   On account of its close linkage with the conditions under which it operates, metabolism must necessarily undergo some changes.   This is the only basis on which the evolution of living systems could take place.

Some changes must have taken place in the metabolism in the process of the individual existence of the earliest living things, even if their external conditions remained completely unchanged, for the very growth of these organisms of itself disturbed the ratio of their volume to their surface.   Only a division of the system into parts, occurring in direct relation to its growth, could restore the lost equilibrium.   In primitive systems such division could, at first, be brought about by external influences.   However, as life developed, internal mechanisms evolved and these ensured the constant active division of the living systems.   We shall devote ourselves to these mechanisms and their origins later.

Here we need only emphasise that the constant growth of the earliest living systems could only occur if it was always associated with their division.   Several experiments carried out in recent years have shown that some contemporary micro-organisms, when repeatedly subcultured, can maintain their metabolism in action and their viability constant through thousands of transplantations, but only if they are cultured artificially, under strictly sterile and unchanging optimal conditions. However, under natural circumstances, where the external conditions cannot be constant, one can always observe regular changes in metabolism in the process of individual development in contemporary organisms, which already show some intracellular differentiation. If the cells of such organisms do not divide for some reason, the original sequence of biological reactions in them is gradually disturbed (the so-called ageing of cells).

In the end this leads to the complete and irreversible decompensation of metabolism. The processes of breakdown (especially the hydrolysis of proteins) begin to predominate to a decisive extent over those of synthesis, and this leads to a disruption of cellular structure and mechanisms, i.e. to the natural death of the cell.

Thus, even in the first stages of the development of life, and especially after the occurrence of the ever-increasing differentiation of organisms, death always was and is the normal and necessary culmination of those qualitative changes in metabolism which take place in any organism in the course of its ontogenetic development.

Thus, from the very beginning there were only two possible courses for any individual system. A living system either grew and divided or else it became old and died. Later these possibilities were somewhat extended. In the first place, at some time in the course of their development, unicellular organisms acquired the ability to form spores or cysts.

When this happens the cell goes over to a state of closed life or anabiosis, which has great biological significance in preserving the organism and enabling it to survive under unfavourable external conditions such as extraordinarily high and low temperatures, decreased moisture etc. The state of anabiosis occurs extensively in living nature. It differs in essence from death in that, when the organism is killed, many of the metabolic reactions continue to go on at the same or sometimes an even greater rate though their co-ordination has been destroyed.

In anabiosis, on the contrary, when cells are desiccated or

deep-frozen, the co-ordination of the metabolic reactions is retained but their rate is gradually and equally reduced to practically nothing.

Thus, when these anabiotic cells are damped or warmed carefully, and also when spores germinate, there is the possibility of restoring these objects to active life but only if the orderly arrangement of metabolism has not been changed qualitatively in the process.

Another factor which extended the opportunities available to the first organisms at some stage in their development was the origin of conjugation, i.e. the union of two individual living systems with similar organisations. For all their similarity, though, the two coalescent systems could not have been absolutely identical in their metabolism. When several different metabolic networks interact within the unified living system, its vital processes are substantially stimulated in some as yet unknown way. This may be observed in cultures of many kinds of micro-organisms; when they multiply steadily for a long time they gradually age and begin to degenerate. However, if conjugation begins to occur within the culture the organisms are, as it were, rejuvenated; they regain their earlier vitality and are again able to go on multiplying for a long time.

Conjugation acquired a special biological significance when, in the course of its development, it became a sexual process in which the systems which united (the gametes or the male and female sex cells) had already become differentiated from one another in respect of their metabolism and the presence in them of heritable properties. When they coalesce to form a zygote (fertilisation of the egg) new forms of metabolism arise and this has a very important influence on the whole of the later development of life. It is just for this reason that sexuality has acquired such a monopolistic position in the reproduction of the great majority of higher organisms.

In the matter of the increase in qualitative complexity of the process of growth, the fact that the growth of living systems has always been closely associated with their development has been of decisive importance. Even though this development was of a comparatively simple nature at first, in the course of time it became more and more complicated with each new advance of the organism to a higher rung on the evolutionary ladder. In this connection, all the attempts, which have been so widely reported in the scientific literature, to describe the growth of higher organisms from its beginning to its end in terms of a single formula or curve, like the curves which express the course of simple physical or chemical processes, have invariably ended in failure.

In essence, biological development consists in the fact that the small changes in metabolism which take place in the process of growth of the living organism always lead, in the end, to some sort of qualitative discontinuity, to a considerable remodelling of various parts of the general network of metabolism. This remodelling also created a potentiality, the ' readiness ' of living things to carry out (under the necessary external conditions) physiological or morphogenetic processes which had previously not been a feature of the cells from which they originated.

We may observe this phenomenon in its simplest form in micro-organisms. For example, some fungi which produce antibiotics only do so in the second phase of mycelial development and their production is therefore associated with some remodelling of metabolism. A similar reconstruction must assuredly precede the division of the microbial cell, and, even more, its differentiation in spore formation.

However, such metabolic changes assumed specially complicated forms and were extremely important biologically as they occurred in multicellular organisms. As we have already seen, even in the most primitive of these (the sponges, for example) there is a certain differentiation of individual cells having particular physiological functions. Such differentiation is, however, only possible when orderly metabolic changes somehow take place in the original cells which started by being uniform, in such a way that when they change the cells have to follow different courses.

Even in its earliest simple form this phenomenon remains substantially unstudied. Obviously there must be far more complicated laws governing the metabolic changes occurring in the individual development of organisms which belong to a higher level on the evolutionary scale.

In the course of its development each contemporary plant must pass through certain definite stages which are necessary parts of its ontogenesis and which follow one another in a strict, orderly sequence, each stage requiring its own particular set of environmental conditions for its completion. According to T. Lysenko these stages are, in essence, qualitatively discontinuous changes in metabolism and form the basis of the ' readiness ' of plants for the occurrence (under suitable environmental conditions) of perceptible phases of morphogenesis (changes of tillering, of flowering etc.).

Similarly, there is reason to believe that, in the embryonic development of animals, visible differentiation of the originally uniform cells of the dividing ovum must be preceded by farreaching changes in their metabolism which, taken as a whole, constitute what is commonly known as ' determination '.

Unfortunately, the present state of our knowledge only allows us to scratch at the surface of these phenomena, only to register the sequence of formation of those morphological structures which arise in the course of embryogenesis. A striking feature of this sequence is that, to a certain extent, it repeats, as it were, the forms of development through which the particular organism passed in the course of its phylogenetic evolution.

As it has sometimes been the custom to say: higher living things ' retain a memory ' as it were, of their remote past and therefore reproduce it in their ontogenesis. But, although this is a very picturesque way of expressing things it doesn't, of course, really explain anything. Furthermore, if we make a purely physical approach to the ' mechanics of embryonic development ' it remains quite incomprehensible why a higher organism should follow approximately the same path in its development from the egg as was followed by its ancestors although, from the point of view of the general laws of mechanics, this is quite unnecessary.

It seems to me that we shall approach some distance towards the solution of this problem if we try to use the biological laws which we called to mind at the beginning of the last chapter.

Higher animals and man accomplish any particular section of their metabolism, e.g. the glycolytic degradation of sugar, by following the strictly determinate sequence of chemical reactions which together account for that section. This does not happen because the higher living thing is ' repeating ' a phenomenon which was characteristic of primitive microbes 1,000,000,000 years ago, but by virtue of a necessity which grew up historically, by virtue of the fact that, for biological forms of organisation there is not and cannot be any other sequence of events in the given section of metabolism although, from the point of view of the ordinary laws of chemistry, one can imagine many other chemical reactions leading to the same result.

Naturally, when we speak of the phenomena of embryonic development in higher organisms, we are not concerned with the simple sequence of reactions in a particular metabolic network, but with the sequence of changes in that sequence, a sequence of the second order, so to speak, a strictly constant succession of obligatory changes in metabolism which lie at the root of the differentiation of the cells of the embryo, as it develops from the ovum. It may, however, be that, even at this very high level of organisation of life, higher organisms bring about the same sequences of phenomena as did their distant ancestors, simply because any other order is biologically impossible although, of course, from a purely physical or mechanical point of view, one can imagine an innumerable multitude of other paths of development.

After the embryonic period of its individual development every highly developed multicellular organism regularly passes through the so-called period of growth, then the period of maturity associated with the reproduction of descendants, and finally the period of ageing with gradual impairment of metabolism leading invariably to its complete decompensation and the death of the organism. During all these periods, higher living things manifest a remarkable efficiency of co-ordination of the growth and development of the organism as a whole, as well as of its various organs, tissues and cells. This co-ordination is regulated by a very complicated group of mechanisms which are mainly humoral in plants but are closely associated with the activity of the nervous system in animals.

We can, to some extent, assess the significance of these mechanisms by artificially isolating cells from their influence in so-called tissue cultures. When all their requirements are satisfied (food supplied, wastes removed etc.) such cells appear to be capable of unlimited growth and division, but the normal relationship between the growth and differentiation of cells is usually impaired in such cases, although not by any means uniformly.

The uncontrolled multiplication of undifferentiated cells can also take place within a complete, undamaged organism. This is the way in which tumours, especially cancerous ones, arise. In this connection the opinion has been expressed that, if we are to find out how to prevent or cure cancer, we must discover the fundamental nature of the growth of cells and the laws governing it, and also the mechanism by which the living body normally exercises its control over the growth and development of cells.

Thus we see that, like the powers of assimilation and excretion, the ability of living things to grow and develop is, in its original, primitive form, derived directly from orderly metabolism. But in the further evolution of organisms this ability too passed through a number of organisational forms of ever increasing complexity which cannot be understood directly, simply by reference to the laws governing inorganic nature.

Growth and development are directly connected with the third of the fundamental properties of organisms which we mentioned earlier, namely their power of 'multiplication'. In its biological aspect, which is the one we shall be examining, the concept of 'multiplication' should not include (as it sometimes does) any increase in numbers of the systems in question. In particular, we do not consider it rational to use the word to denote an increase in the number of molecules in the course of some chemical process, whether it be a single chemical reaction taking place in a gas or in solution, or a whole series of interrelated reactions in some complicated system, such as the formation of lactic acid in the process of glycolysis. It is self-evident that what we have here is not multiplication but continuous formation of molecules of lactic acid. In so far as we differ in this respect from very many contemporary authors, we doubt very much whether it is correct to use the term 'multiplication' in its biological sense in reference to the phenomenon of the continual formation of new viral nucleoprotein in the course of the co-ordinated metabolic reactions of the living cells of tobacco leaves.

This phenomenon is very similar to 'multiplication' in

that it requires the presence of ready-made nucleic acid molecules for its occurrence. However, in this case the metabolic process which underlies any biological multiplication belongs, not to the virus, but to the living multimolecular system of the tobacco leaf. The virus only alters the nature of the metabolism somewhat.

In view of the evolutionary path which led to the origin of life, it is reasonable to take, as an inorganic prototype of biological ' multiplication ', a process of mechanical sub-division of multimolecular systems, similar to the process of formation of drops in an emulsion when it is shaken. The drops of the earliest coacervates might also have been broken up in a similar way by breaking waves or surf, even before they had evolved into living things. With the origin of life, how-ever, this passive process of dispersal of the original systems must have been exchanged in the first organisms for the active division of living bodies.

This did not occur until some sort of metabolism, perhaps of the most primitive kind, had been formed in the living systems. One could represent this process of active division schematically as follows. As a result of synthetic processes, polymers, such as proteins or even simple starch, accumulated within the living system at the expense of the substances in the external medium. Later there was an orderly shift of meta-bolism within the system, which strengthened the processes of hydrolysis in it. As a result the polymer was broken down and there was rapid formation of an osmotically active sub-stance (e.g. sugar) in the system. If the rate of formation of this substance exceeded the rate of its diffusion into the external medium, a high osmotic pressure was created within the system and this, in the end, broke the system into pieces. When metabolism shifted back these parts grew again and once more accumulated polymers and then were broken to pieces again etc.

With the formation of surface membranes and after the origin of mechanisms for harnessing energy, the phenomenon of active division of living bodies must have assumed more complicated forms, associated with the rhythmic structural changes in the proteins of the membrane when they interacted with ATP.

It has been possible to show, in contemporary living bodies, that this sort of interaction involves dephosphorylation of ATP and that the energy thus liberated is used in the process of active division of the cell, which is markedly endothermic.

The internal structure of a coacervate drop is more or less uniform and therefore the pieces into which it divides are essentially alike. However, once life had come into existence, the internal differentiation of living systems became greater and greater and therefore the main difficulty in multiplication was the necessity for each of the daughter systems to retain its original composition and structure, that is to say, to bring about the division in such a way as to form parts which would differ from the original system only in size and mass, not in organisation. The more highly differentiated the protoplasmic organelles the more complicated the solution of this problem, which could only be achieved by the evolutionary creation of qualitatively new mechanisms which had not been present in the primitive living systems.

The extreme complexity and efficiency of these mechanisms was developed in connection with the formation of the nucleus of the cell. As we have already seen, there is, as yet, no clearly differentiated nucleus in the blue-green algae or in certain species of bacteria. In these organisms the nuclear material is simply distributed in the centre of the protoplast in the form of individual formed bodies made of DNA. Even here, however, we may find characteristic changes of the bodies, associated with the redistribution of nuclear material, in the preparation of the protoplast for division.

At a higher level of evolutionary development the overall division of the cell is preceded by the orderly process of nuclear division. This process attains its highest degree of perfection in mitosis, which is the means by which the amazingly accurate apportionment of nuclear material between the daughter cells is accomplished.

When mitosis begins there is a profound change in the nuclear material, leading to the appearance of visible chromosomes, which are bodies containing DNA. These then arrange themselves in the equatorial plane of the cell and each divides into two lengthwise. The daughter chromosomes thus formed separate from one another and each set gathers together at one

*Figure 16 follows page 52.

pole of the cell where the new nuclei are formed; the cytoplasm also becomes divided.

The accurate distribution of nuclear material became specially important with the development of the sexual process which can, as a rule, only occur when there is an accurate correspondence between the components of the gametes which are fusing with one another. The formation of gametes is, therefore, always preceded by a so-called reduction division, in which each sex cell only obtains a half set of chromosomes, so that the complete set of chromosomes characteristic of the species in question is restored when the gametes fuse to form the zygote. It follows that the development of mitosis must be regarded as a prerequisite for the origin of sexual multiplication.

An exact description of mitosis may be found in any text-book of cytology. Its successive phases have been studied morphologically in the greatest detail. However, the nature of the factors which effect the process and the mechanisms underlying it are still a closed book to us. It is clear that this form of multiplication, which occurs in most contemporary cells, already shows a very high degree of organisational complexity. One cannot therefore simply discuss it in terms of ordinary physical and chemical laws, sliding over any study of its evolutionary origin, as many contemporary authors try to do.

This applies still more forcibly to the way in which multi-cellular organisms multiply, which is even more complicated, and different from simple cell division. This process is not only based on the processes of growth, division and differentiation of cells, but also on the process of ontogenetic development of the whole organism as a single, integral system.

It is neither possible nor necessary to describe here the astonishing variety of forms of vegetative and sexual reproduction which exist in the animal and vegetable world. Such descriptions can easily be found in textbooks of zoology and botany. Here we need only take account of the differences in principle between the multiplication of unicellular creatures and that of higher animals and plants. In the simple division of unicellular organisms there is direct reproduction by them of something which is like themselves. On the other hand, when multicellular organisms multiply, that which is " like themselves " is reproduced in their posterity only, to use a figurative expression of T. Lysenko, " by means of a long chain of transformations of that which is unlike itself ", i.e. as the result of the passage of the organism along a long path of development, at the various stages of which the organism as a whole undergoes profound, qualitative changes, thereby ceasing to be what it was before. The laws governing this extremely important vital phenomenon still await study and establishment.

Closely associated with the powers of growth and multiplication of living bodies was their power of self-reproduction, which was, as we have already seen, in its primitive form directly derived from metabolism. The phenomenon of self-reproduction is based on the fact that the organism receives, from the external medium, compounds which are foreign to it in their chemical nature, and transforms them into substances which are identical with those already in itself. Even quite recently the view was widely supported in the scientific literature that the continual formation of particular substances within the organism was entirely determined by the presence of ready-made samples of these substances in the material of the genes of the organism in question. These sample molecules were supposed to ' multiply ' and thus to ensure the constancy of structure and composition of the organism. I can remember how a whole department of a well-established scientific research institute worked for a long time in vain, trying to find even a trace of nicotine in tobacco seeds, because, if it were absent it would be impossible to explain the presence of nicotine in the grown plant.

However, the evidence of contemporary biochemistry has decisively refuted this opinion and has disclosed completely different mechanisms for the constancy of biochemical syntheses, based on the constancy of particular sequences of biochemical reactions. We find the formation of lactic and butyric acids in certain species of bacteria, of chlorophyll, anthocyanins and alkaloids in higher plants, of vitamins in yeast cells and streptomycin in actinomycetes, not because ready-made samples of these substances were already present in these objects, but because, at a given stage in their life cycle, particular chemical reactions occur in them in a strictly determinate and integrated sequence. In particular, the nicotine in the roots of the tobacco plant develops afresh only when the differentiation of particular cells in them has led to the creation of the metabolic sequence required for its biosynthesis.

The constancy of the formation of those substances which are characteristic of a particular living body is merely a reflection of the constancy of the order in which one reaction follows another in that body. This is no ' self-reproduction ' of molecules in the strict meaning of the expression, it is only a strictly constant new formation of them. The sequence of reactions on which this new formation is based does not depend on any single factor, but is in itself an expression of the whole organisation of the protoplasm of the organism in question in its interaction with the external world.

As we have already shown, some constancy in the sequence of metabolic reactions must have arisen even in the very earliest stages of the formation of life, for easily changed, highly unstable systems were constantly exposed to the risk of losing their dynamic stability, which meant their disappearance. The process of selection occurring in the course of their further evolution, therefore, only preserved those original systems in which the reactions of the metabolic network were integrated to form stationary, constantly repetitive chains and cycles.

Even on this primitive basis the first organisms acquired the power of continually synthesising compounds with such a relatively complicated structure as, for example, the coenzymes or ATP which they required. Alongside this there took place the gradual stabilisation of the amino acid sequence in the structure of the protein-like polymers.

The importance of this latter factor became markedly greater when the increases in length and complexity of the metabolic chains gave rise to the necessity for very accurate co-ordination of the rates of the reactions which comprised the multiple links of the chains. This could only be attained after the emergence of enzymes, i.e. proteins which possessed a strictly determinate mutual relationship between certain atomic groups within their molecules. As we now know, this is achieved, not merely by the presence of a definite order of distribution of amino acid residues in the polypeptide chain, but by the nature of the folding of the chain in the protein globule.

It would seem that the sequence of metabolic reactions, the organisation of living bodies in time which formed the basis for their primary ability to reproduce themselves, was not on its own, enough for this purpose. At some particular higher stage in the evolutionary development of life, the spatial organisation or configuration of the macromolecules of RNA and the ribonucleic granules which it formed assumed a particular significance in reproduction.

The important part played by RNA in the synthesis of specifically constructed proteins, enzymes in particular, is confirmed by many facts which have been discovered recently. However, this part can only be played against the background of a particular metabolic network, as is shown by the example of the synthesis of the tobacco virus to which we have already referred more than once. RNA is, thus, not some exclusive and independent factor which entirely determines the ability of living things to reproduce themselves. This ability is, in the first place, bound up with the organisation of metabolism which arose at an earlier stage in the process of evolutionary development, and RNA is an important, though supplementary mechanism, a superstructure of more recent origin which, however, raised the organisation to a new and higher level.

The next step in the same direction was the origin of DNA, which is not directly required for the uniform synthesis of proteins. This may be seen in the case of a fragment of the alga *Acetabularia* without a nucleus, which retains for months the ability to synthesise proteins and RNA without having any nuclear material (fig. 17).*

However, by virtue of its great metabolic inertia, DNA is an important stabilising factor. The need for such a stabiliser increased specially fast when the increasing complexity of the extremely labile metabolic network gave rise to a situation where a single dynamic stability, by itself, became insufficient for the accurate self-reproduction of the living system in its division.

There is no cause to doubt that, as a rule, the DNA synthesised in contemporary living things exactly reproduces

*Figure 17 follows page 52.

the structure of that which previously existed in the nucleus of the cell. We can find some explanation of this fact in the enzymic syntheses of polynucleotides which have recently been carried out by S. Ochoa, M. Grunberg-Manago, A. Kornberg and others. These syntheses are only successful in the presence of ready-made specimens of the polynucleotide being synthesised. One may therefore suppose that, in the living cell, the protoplasmic enzymes synthesise new molecules of DNA, which have the same highly specific structure as those which were already present as components of the nucleus of the cell.

Contemporary biochemical studies indicate that DNA is an extremely passive compound in metabolism. It accumulates in any growing cell and is, as it were, excluded from the metabolism so that, when the cell later divides, it is transferred to the daughter cells unchanged, in the form ˙n which it was synthesised in the mother cell. This is undoubtedly a very important factor in the self-reproduction of organisms in their descendants. However, we remain completely in the dark as to the actual way by which this constancy of the structure of DNA can ensure the invariable occurrence in the daughter cell of the same metabolic sequences of reactions which were to be found in the mother cell. This, however, is the crux of the problem of the self-reproduction of living things at the stage of evolution which we can now observe.

The general idea is that the DNA present in the cell determines, in some virtually unknown way, the synthesis of specific proteins, especially enzymes. It is assumed that DNA either serves directly as a matrix for this synthesis, or it passes on via RNA the ' information ' necessary for this synthesis, which exists in ' code ' in the actual structure of the DNA. Thus, this structure determines the formation of a constant set of enzymes and, therefore, a constant and specific sequence of reactions in the metabolic network.

For the present, however, this sort of hypothesis is only based on more or less ingenious analogies and on very indirect evidence. There have been no biochemical studies in which the phenomena postulated have been reproduced. On the contrary, there are quite a few facts which would tend rather to contradict than to confirm the hypothesis. For example, it has recently been shown that, in bacteria, which are, of course, very rich in ready-made nucleic acids, the synthesis of proteins is markedly hindered, or even suspended altogether, if the microbes being studied do not receive materials, which are not needed for the synthesis of proteins, but are necessary for the formation of nucleic acids. This gives one the impression that the specificity of protein synthesis is determined, not by ready-made particles of nucleic acid which contain a specific code, but by the actual process of their reproduction in the course of normal metabolism.

In order to show that there can be other hypotheses than those already mentioned concerning the part played by DNA in the self-reproduction of living systems, I will permit myself (using the author's privilege) to set out briefly the observations which were published recently by Commoner.

As a cell grows there is constant formation of DNA going on against a background of general metabolism. The composition and structure of this DNA correspond precisely with those of the nuclear DNA already present in the cell which is here playing the part of a primer. In the course of their formation the molecules of DNA extract from the general metabolic complex various mono-, di- and polynucleotides which are continually being synthesised there, in definite amounts and definite proportions, and which play a very important part in metabolism as coenzymes, mediators etc. The removal of these active substances from the general metabolism in the synthesis of nucleic acid is accomplished in an order which is strictly specific for the DNA in question and in strictly determinate quantitative ratios. Thus, it is not the finished molecule of DNA which specifically influences the metabolism, but the actual process of its formation. After it has been formed the DNA is excluded from the metabolism and, so to speak put into reserve, 'into cold storage' where it is preserved unchanged and thus passed on to the new cell where it once more acts as a primer in the synthesis of new amounts of DNA, thus regulating its metabolism just as it did that of the mother cell.

In the same way as its own DNA must act as a primer, so also, would a foreign DNA if it could gain admission to the cell unchanged. Perhaps this is what does happen in experiments in which one strain of bacteria is transformed into another by the introduction of DNA isolated from the latter into the former.

From the point of view of the hypothesis just put forward, it is the whole metabolic complex, the living system as a whole, which possesses the power of self-reproduction. This power arose at the very beginning of the establishment of metabolism, long before the appearance of DNA, and had nothing to do with it. However, the appearance of DNA was a very important stage in the evolution of the property of living things with which we are dealing. It raised the power of self-reproduction to a very high level of organisation, ensuring a certain conservatism, a lasting constancy of composition, structure and metabolism during the division of the increasingly complicated living things. But this, of course, does not in any way mean that one can reduce the whole complicated phenomenon of biological self-reproduction just to the ' multiplication ' of molecules of DNA.

The power of self-reproduction lies at the basis of the phenomenon of heredity, but the latter concept is far wider than the former. Heredity consolidates the experiences of all preceding generations.

Therefore, the longer the evolutionary way of phylogenetic development an organism has followed and the higher a living being stands on the evolutionary scale, the more complicated the forms assumed by its heredity.

In the most primitive unicellular organisms heredity amounts essentially to the maintenance of their characteristic metabolic sequence during their incessant growth and multiplication. At this stage of evolution, therefore, the phenomenon of self-reproduction plays a dominant part in heredity.

However, as the organisation of living things becomes more complicated, the process of development, with its radical shifts in metabolism, becomes more important in connection with their heredity. In the cycle of development of multicellular organisms there is a definite sequence of changes in sequence of metabolic reactions which we have already referred to as a sequence of the second order. This is an essential aspect of the heredity of highly developed living things, which is not concerned simply with the retention of a constant sequence of metabolic reactions, but is mainly directed towards the maintenance of the invariability of a sequence of regular changes in metabolism as the organism passes through the stages of its individual development. As we have already seen, the basis of this sequence is retained in the same form in which it was elaborated in the process of phylogenetic development over the long series of preceding generations. It cannot depend on any one single factor but reflects the organisation of the living being as it has been elaborated historically.

Therefore, whatever changes in nuclear material or DNA we may induce, we shall never succeed, to put it crudely, in turning an elephant into a fly or, conversely, a fly into an elephant. In the changes which we can observe directly in our researches on heredity, we are only dealing with the superstructures and alterations which have been laid down on top of the basic sequence of development to supplement it. We are here dealing with a sequence of the third order, if one may express it so. Of course, what we have said is still a long way from providing a satisfactory description of the phenomenon of heredity as a whole, but it does, at least, give some indication of the way in which this property is more complicated in highly developed organisms than the power of reproduction which originally came into being when life first appeared. We must also bear in mind that, of all the possibilities inherent in the hereditary basis of the organism, the only ones which will be realised are those for which the necessary conditions are present in the environment. Heredity can, therefore, arise at a given stage of evolution of living matter only on the basis of the unity of the organism and its environment.

As we have already seen, the energy which arises as the result of the occurrence of exoergic reactions in living bodies, is used in them for a number of different purposes, for the active extraction of substances from the external medium, for the synthesis of the ingredients making up their protoplasm, for the growth and multiplication of organisms, for the osmotic, electric and even luminous activities which occur in them. This is expressed specially clearly in the transformation of chemical energy into another form, that of mechanical motion, the power of the organism to move about in space.

This power originated in the very earliest period of the existence of life and may therefore be regarded as one of the fundamental properties of all living things. It is true that many contemporary living things do not have the power of moving visibly about in space, but even in such cases the protoplasm in their cells moves and circulates fairly actively. Furthermore, living bodies are constantly moving slowly as they grow and multiply.

The active translocation of living bodies relative to their environment may be accomplished in one of four ways, it may be amoeboid, ciliary, flagellar or muscular. The last of these, depending on muscular contraction, is the most modern form of movement and is characteristic of the most highly developed organisms, which have highly differentiated tissues, specifically adapted to the performance of this function. Here, of course, the phenomenon manifests itself in its most complicated form. However, in the history of science, matters have been made more complicated by the fact that this is the form of biological movement which has been studied for the longest time and with the greatest intensity, while the more primitive forms have hardly received any serious study.

It is only recently that this deficiency has been made good. In doing so people have often applied evidence, obtained from systems which are certainly far more complicated even if better studied, to the assessment of the more primitive forms of movement.

Obviously the reversible alteration in shape, water-retaining power and other properties of protein particles and, later, even the arrangement of these particles relative to one another in protein aggregates, represent the primary event in any biological movement. All these phenomena are directly associated with the chemical interaction between proteins and ATP, which is dephosphorylated and serves as a source of energy for the mechanical movement.

This sort of direct conversion of chemical energy into mechanical energy could have arisen even in the original, open, protein systems, when the energy released in them owing to the transfer of hydrogen stopped being simply dissipated in the form of heat and began to be accumulated in the high-energy bonds of ATP. The later evolutionary improvement of this process consisted, in the first place, in a speeding up of the reactions associated with the accumulation and transfer of energy, and, in the second place, in the structural orderliness of the relative positions of the protein micelles in their aggregates.

In the simplest case, the energy liberated during the degradation of ATP is used in converting the protein of the protoplasm (especially its superficial layer) into the gel state. Evidence available at present indicates that the superficial layer of protoplasm contains proteins which can react with ATP. The energy thus set free is used to keep up the tension in the cortical layer, on which the form and tonus of the cell depend. A change in this tension can lead to movement. Obviously such phenomena form the basis of movements, particularly those of some plants.

There is reason to suppose that the change of protoplasmic proteins from gel to sol and back again is responsible for the so-called amoeboid motion characteristic of the plasmodia of the slime fungi or myxomycetes, of amoebae and of other similar biological objects. In amoeboid motion there is an extrusion of larger or smaller protuberances of protoplasm (the pseudopodia) in the direction of the movement. After this the rest of the living mass flows into these protuberances and thus moves in relation to its substrate. It has been shown that the plasmodium of fungi contains a specific protein, known as mycomyosin, which can react with ATP. When this happens, the ATP is dephosphorylated and the viscosity of the mycomyosin is markedly lowered, and then gradually returns to its previous level. The formation of pseudopodia is usually regarded as taking place in the following way. The protoplasmic gel at the moving end of the body liquefies while there is contraction of the cortical gel at the ' tail '. This drives the liquid protoplasm into the pseudopodium.

Thus, where there is amoeboid movement there are still no differentiated parts of the living body specifically carrying out the function of transporting the organism in space. Where there is ciliary or flagellar motion such differentiation has already taken place. Cilia, which are numerous motile outgrowths of cells, are very widely distributed among the most diverse representatives of the living world, both in unicellular and in multicellular organisms. Flagella are specific cellular organelles and are to be met with in a few unicellular organisms, in the spermatozoa of most animals and lower plants, in the zoospores of algae etc.

These two types of formation are in many ways similar to one another but, all the same, the movement of flagella is more highly organised and more complicated. In particular, flagella can move, not only like oars (which is characteristic of cilia), but also like propellers.

In spite of a great deal of experimental and descriptive evidence, the mechanism of movement of cilia and flagella is still far from clear. The only thing that can be stated with conviction is that, here too, the source of energy for the mechanical movement is the dephosphorylation of ATP by specific proteins in the protoplasm. Cilia and flagella usually behave as independent effectors but, in the course of the evolutionary development of organisms, they have fallen more and more under the control of the nervous system. Thus, both from the point of view of the presence of specific differentiated organelles, and from the point of view of the emergence of some sort of regulation, ciliary and flagellar movement undoubtedly represent considerable steps forward by comparison with amoeboid movement. However, the ability of the organism to move by muscular contraction has achieved an extreme efficiency. It is so far superior to all other forms of movement in both speed and power that we are fully justified in regarding it as a new property, which only arose at a comparatively high stage of the evolutionary development of the animal world. When this happened the contractility inherent in protoplasm became the essential function of highly differentiated cells or multinuclear complexes— muscle fibres—with a very complicated specific structure. The muscle fibres did not acquire this structure suddenly, but comparative anatomy and histology enable us to form an opinion as to the way in which their structural elements changed in the course of evolution, gradually becoming better and better adapted to the performance of their functions.

The visceral muscles have a comparatively simple structure. They consist of small, elongated fusiform cells, each with one nucleus. Characteristically they undergo rhythmically repeated contractions which may be completely independent of the nervous system although, in higher organisms, they are controlled by the autonomic nervous system.

In lower invertebrates, such as the coelenterates, the body muscles are rather similar to visceral muscles and undergo the same characteristic rhythmic pulsation. On ascending the scale of evolution this structure becomes more complicated, but even in the worms and lower molluscs it is still comparatively simple. Only in the higher invertebrates, such as the cephalopod molluscs or the insects, does its complexity approach that of the muscles of the trunk and skeleton of vertebrates. These so-called striated muscles are very highly differentiated structures in which the contractile properties have reached an amazingly high level of development particularly as regards the speed and power of contraction.

There is reason to believe that such functional excellence could not have been achieved simply as a result of single changes occurring at the multimolecular level. There can be no doubt that, in muscular work, the movements, relative to one another, of the proteins aggregated in the structure of the muscle fibre, are of great importance.

The most important of these proteins are actin and myosin. According to V. Engel'gardt and M. Lyubimova myosin is the enzyme which dephosphorylates ATP. Together they form a complex, actomyosin, in which there is a definite spatial orientation of the component molecules. Many attempts have been made to reproduce the work of a muscle in models specifically constructed from actomyosin. If ATP is added to threads of actomyosin they will contract and do work, the ATP being used up in the process. The thread then relaxes and can again be made to contract by the addition of ATP. Thus, in this model, actomyosin plays the part of an adenosine triphosphatase, liberating the energy of ATP and thus causing contraction of the thread.

Nevertheless, even the best of the actomyosin models so far constructed cannot form a complete analogy with the muscle fibril. It is clear that the structure of the latter is far more highly organised and its contraction is associated with the orderly migration of molecules of myosin and actin or complexes of them. The regulation of the contraction of skeletal muscles is also extremely complicated and highly organised; it is carried out by the nervous system.

IRRITABILITY AND NERVOUS ACTIVITY

In many cases mechanical movement is the most obvious expression of irritability, which is a property common to all living things. Irritability is usually taken to mean the ability of an organism to respond to an environmental stimulus by a reaction which, in force, place and character does not correspond with the force, place and character of the stimulus itself. This reaction of organisms differs fundamentally from similar phenomena in non-living nature by reason of its reversibility. The discharge of energy in an inorganic system (e.g. the explosion of gunpowder) is not followed by the spontaneous restoration of the original state of the system. In organisms, on the other hand, this restoration does occur so that the reaction to a stimulus can, as a rule, be repeated many times.

It is hard to say how much justification there is for the attempts of various contemporary authors to discover phenomena analogous with biological irritability even at the unimolecular level of the evolutionary development of matter. One may, however, suppose that the multimolecular open systems, which we have taken to form the basis for the origin of life, as soon as they had acquired some form of metabolism, however primitive, possessed the power of reacting specifically to the influence of the external medium by which they were surrounded. When once processes leading to the accumulation of energy (e.g. in the form of ATP) had arisen, then they immediately acquired the possibility of discharging this energy in response to some external stimulus. This must have led to colloid-chemical changes in the coacervate systems, in particular, to changes in the degree of dispersal of the protein-like complexes present in them, also changes in viscosity and adsorptive powers, i.e. to all those phenomena which we see even now when the protoplasm of a cell is irritated. However, in the original systems, as in contemporary protoplasm, energy was accumulated again. Owing to the incessant metabolic reactions occurring in them, there was a fresh accumulation of energy as a result of which the system returned to its original state.

If this were not so, the original systems would have been constantly subject to the risk of disappearance; thus the effect of natural selection was specially clearly manifested in this matter. As a result of its action the further evolutionary development of irritability, as a primary, elementary characteristic of everything living, acquired quite a definite direction and, on this basis, there arose a new and special property of these primary organisms, namely excitability, which was already markedly adaptive in nature and which enabled organisms to carry out particular actions in response to the influence of the outside world.

The ability of living things to get into an excited state under the influence of external or internal stimuli manifests itself first of all in active (occurring at the expense of internal reserves of energy) reversal of the sequence and intensity of metabolic reactions. These changes are, however, closely associated with a number of structural, physical and physicochemical changes characteristic of the excitation of protoplasm. Among them we must take particular notice of bioelectric phenomena (the bioelectric potentials and action currents). Formerly action currents were supposed to occur only in nervous and muscular tissue, where they play the chief part in the functioning of these highly differentiated systems. However, it has now been shown that bioelectric potentials also arise in any undifferentiated protoplasm such as myxomycetes, amoebae, algae etc.

It is characteristic of the most primitive unicellular organisms that excitation only arises in them in response to the immediate, direct action of the medium. The zone of excitation corresponds with the region stimulated by the irritant, while the excitation itself only develops very slowly and has no marked tendency to spread.

However, the evolutionary development of living things was directed towards the emergence and improvement of a process for extending the excitation, as this enabled the association between the organism and its environment to be strengthened.   When multicellular organisms began to exist, the extension of excitation assumed a specially great importance. The evidence of comparative physiology discloses the route by which this phenomenon was gradually improved in the process of the evolution of life.   In organisms which have no nervous system, such as plants, the spreading of excitability proceeds essentially from cell to cell, especially by the transfer of the specific metabolic products arising as a result of the stimulation. This is the way in which the excitation of parts of the body far away from the site of stimulation occurs in organisms at this stage of evolution.

In its original form this type of transfer of excitation is still very unsatisfactory as it occurs at what is, comparatively speaking, a very slow rate.   Even on this basis, considerable increases in the rate of transfer of excitation could be achieved in the course of evolution, but the essential advance in this respect was only accomplished by the origin and development of the nervous system with its specialised functions of receiving stimuli and transferring excitation.   This was an exceedingly important event in the evolution of life.   It determined the whole of the further development of the animal world, in which the nervous system has played the leading part in integrating organisms with the world around them.

As we have already shown, in primitive organisms irritability and the excitability arising out of it are still not differentiated, they are not localised and are present in a more or less equal degree in all parts of the body.   They can react to a stimulus from the external world only by direct contact with the source of the stimulus.   Morphologically and physiologically differentiated nervous systems give rise to incomparably greater possibilities of reacting at a distance.   It was on the basis of such systems that the organism acquired the capacity to orientate itself in time and space, which led to an immeasurable extension of its opportunities, the sphere in which it could exist. Comparative physiology teaches us how the nervous system developed rapidly and progressively in the course of the evolution of the animal kingdom.   Even at a comparatively early stage, the interaction between the organism and the environment led, in the first place, to a certain dispersal of the primary, general sensibility of living bodies and to the appearance of specialised formations in particular parts of the body, differentially receiving various forms of external stimulus. The origin of these so-called receptors (or sense organs) was closely associated in the process of the evolution of life, on the one hand with the formation of specialised nervous pathways along which excitation is transmitted, and, on the other, with the establishment of special aggregations of nerve cells within the organism towards which the nervous pathways are directed. These aggregations were the rudiments of the central nervous system. The functional importance of this system is determined by its two-sided connections. It is connected by the afferent nerves to the receptors and therefore also to the stimuli which they receive from the external and internal environment. On the other side, by means of the so-called efferent nerves, the central nervous system acts on the various working organs, or effectors, of the living body such as the muscles, glands of various sorts etc. The activity of these effectors is thus under the control of the central nervous system and is regulated by it.

This sort of organisation of the nervous system provided the conditions for the appearance of a qualitatively new way in which the organism could ward off any stimuli reaching it from the external world. In contradistinction to the blunderbuss reaction of organisms to stimuli in the pre-nervous period, after the development of the nervous system there was differentiated reception of stimuli from the environment by specialised receptors (organs of hearing, sight, touch etc.), transfer of the excitation by the nervous centre and responsive reaction by the organism carried out by specialised effector organs in obedience to signals reaching them from the centre along the efferent conduction routes. This process, which is very important in the physiology of animals, is called a reflex.

In its most primitive form, a reflex consists in a constant, unconditional response of the organism to external stimulation, the stimulus received being passed automatically through the nervous centre to particular organs. In the course of the evolution of animals, however, there was not only a far-reaching adaptation of receptors and effectors to the differential reception of external and internal stimuli and to carrying out the appropriate responses to them. There was also a great improvement in the way in which the numerous and varied forms of stimulus were reorganised in the central regions of the nervous system, so that the signals reaching the effectors from it were highly appropriate in their nature. This depended on the ability to make a detailed analysis and synthesis of various manifestations of the external world and the ever changing conditions within the organism itself.

This being so, the development of the central nervous system (brain and spinal cord) acquired peculiarly great significance in improving the specialised communications between the organism and its environment. It was this which formed the basis for the higher nervous activity of animals and man.

According to the teaching of I. P. Pavlov, the higher nervous activity of highly organised animals is based on conditioned reflexes, i.e. reflexes of a high order and of a qualitatively peculiar kind. They are brought into being in the course of an individual lifetime and are based on inborn or unconditioned reflexes. Unlike these, conditioned reflexes are ephemeral. They are sensitive to all sorts of changes in the internal and external environment of the organism and altogether dependent on them. Owing to this characteristic they are an extremely flexible, labile and precise means of adapting the organism to an ever-changing environment. As I. P. Pavlov wrote: " The animal world as a system can only exist in nature by incessantly balancing itself against its environment, i.e. by virtue of the particular reactions of the living system to stimuli reaching it from outside, which in higher animals are pre-eminently carried out with the help of the nervous system in the form of reflexes ". Later he writes: " . . . if the association between an external agent and the response of the organism to it is constant, it is reasonable to call it an unconditioned reflex; if this association is only temporary we call it a conditioned reflex." Pavlov considered that the adaptation of the organism to its environment, achieved with the help of unconditioned reflexes, " would be effective only if the external environment were absolutely constant. However, as the external environment is extremely varied and, furthermore, is in continual fluctuation, unconditioned associations, being constant associations, are not enough and need to be supplemented by temporary, conditioned reflexes ".

In the course of the historical development of animals the relationship between unconditioned and conditioned reflexes has been changing all the time in favour of the latter. Inborn modes of action predominate over conditioned reflexes in the behaviour of invertebrates and lower vertebrates. In higher animals there is a predominance of conditioned reflexes which are always getting more complicated and more effective.

The higher nervous activity of animals is a set of conditioned reflexes of many and various kinds, which are formed in the course of individual development. Pavlov particularly attributes the way in which people feel, see and understand their environment to the action of conditioned reflexes. Thus, conditioned reflex activity, the primary signalling system of reality, is common to both animals and man.

However, as man's working activity and social life has developed, signals of the second degree have come into being, developed and become extremely efficient. They are signals of these primary signals in the form of words, pronounced, heard and seen. This qualitatively new secondary signalling system is, in fact, found only in man. According to Pavlov these signals of signals are, as it were, generalisations and abstractions from reality. " They are abstractions from reality and allow us to form generalisations which constitute our extra, particularly human, higher thought, giving rise first to common sense, and, finally, to science, the instrument to which man owes his superior orientation in regard to the outer world and to himself."

Here, however, the region of the biological development of matter is exchanged for a new form of its motion, that of the social life of people.

CHAPTER V

CONCLUSION

WHAT conclusions can we draw from all the material we have surveyed?

Life is a special and very complicated form of the motion of matter.

It arose as a new property of matter which it had not possessed earlier, but this only occurred at a particular period in the existence of our planet and resulted from its orderly development.

On Earth, life is represented by an immense number of separate individual systems called organisms. It is only present in these organisms and none of the rest of the objects of our terrestrial world possess it. Thus, one must not think of life outside of organisms, as an abstraction, independent of living bodies.

It is very probable that life does not exist on the majority of the heavenly bodies; after all, there was no life, even on our Earth, for a long period of its existence. One may suppose that, in the illimitable spaces of the Universe, there exist many, extremely highly developed and complicated forms of motion of matter about which we have, at present, no idea. However, it is by no means necessary that all these higher forms of the development of matter should be identical with life, because, of course, the actual processes of development on the various heavenly bodies have been and are widely different. However, among the countless multitude of such bodies there must certainly be some, if only a few, which followed roughly the same evolutionary pathways as our Earth. We have, therefore, no right to regard our Earth as the only abode of life. Identical forms of the motion of matter must exist on other planets too, whether close to us or far away. However, only cosmic flights and journeys could give a direct answer to this problem. We cannot understand life simply and solely by a study of the properties of individual organisms as they exist now, without reference to their earlier history. In particular, not even a thorough analysis of the physical and chemical phenomena going on in living bodies is enough to give us such understanding. A true understanding of the essential nature of life is only possible in the light of a knowledge of its origin and development.

Study of this problem shows that, during the earliest period of the existence of our planet the processes of evolutionary development taking place on it were entirely governed by the laws of physics and chemistry alone. The gradual increase in complexity of the first organic compounds, which occurred under these conditions, gave rise to a state in which the waters of the seas and oceans of that time were converted into what has been referred to as a ' nutrient broth ', that is, into a solution of protein-like compounds and other similar compounds of high molecular weight.

However, when these compounds separated out from the general solution in the form of colloidal multimolecular systems (e.g. coacervate droplets) demarcated from it, the prerequisites for the interaction of these systems with their environment had come into being. The further evolution of these individual organic systems thus began to be controlled by natural selection, a new law which had previously not existed in nature, which came into being in the actual course of the establishment of life and was therefore biological in its nature.

Owing to the action of natural selection, the only systems which were preserved for further existence and development were those which had an internal organisation which became better and better adapted to constant self-preservation and self-reproduction under the prevailing conditions of the environment. Thus there arose that clearly defined interaction between living bodies and the world around them, and also the adaptation or ' purposiveness ' of structure which is so characteristic of all living objects without exception and which runs like a red thread through the whole development of life, right from its origins to the present day.

The paths followed by life in its further evolution are also incomprehensible on the basis of physical and chemical laws alone for, out of the extremely wide field of possibilities open to it under these laws, life has only pursued strictly selective directions which were dictated by an historically determined necessity.

For this reason the formation of the organisation in both space and time which is characteristic of every contemporary living thing, the laying of the foundations of biological metabolism and cellular structure, can only be understood by studying the history of the evolution of life and the establishment of the biological laws specifically governing this evolution.

The laying of these foundations required many, many hundreds of millions of years of the process of the development of life, maybe half of the time for which life has existed on the Earth. Therefore, any attempt at the direct, artificial reproduction or synthesis of even the simplest of living things must still be regarded as very naïve. Obviously the synthesis of life would have to start from those systems which formed the starting point of the development of life on the Earth.

A number of properties which are possessed by all living things now known to us are derived directly from their metabolism and from the extremely delicate structure which is peculiar to them. These properties, taken together, differentiate the organism qualitatively from the objects of the inorganic world. Among them are the ability of living things to absorb substances actively and selectively from their surroundings and to excrete the products of their metabolism back into those surroundings. Also, their powers of growth, multiplication, self-reproduction, locomotion and finally, that property characteristic of everything living, the responsive reaction of organisms to external influences—their irritability.

In the process of the further development of organisms each of these properties has not only become more and more complicated, but has also been metamorphosed into qualitatively new forms of manifestations of life. As the evolution of life did not follow a single channel, but developed along many branching lines, the new manifestations arising are not present in the whole of the living world but only in one or another part of it. We must not, however, ignore them if we want to produce an exhaustive picture of life.

The further the evolution of living things proceeded the more these new manifestations of life acquired a complicated, biologically determined character. They could not, therefore, be mechanically likened to the elementary processes of inorganic nature, ignoring the course of evolution of living material. We can only attain a real understanding of them if we study the history of their development from more primitive forms of biological organisation.

Unfortunately we must admit that our progress in understanding life is still very limited. This is mainly because, even now, many scientists adopt a metaphysical approach to the problem, ignoring the evolutionary route to its solution.

It is characteristic of the evolutionary development of matter that it is going on faster and faster, as it were, following a steeply ascending curve. The accomplishment of the abiogenic evolution of organic substances required several thousands of millions of years. When once life had arisen the development went on far more quickly. Substantial changes in the course of the evolution of life occurred in hundreds or tens of millions of years. The emergence and development of man has taken only one million years in all. Social reorganisations occur within thousands of years or centuries and we can now observe tremendous events and developments in human life occurring over periods of ten years.

We must always bear this law of development in mind in analysing events in the distant past as well as in our forecasts for the future.

When a new form of the motion of matter comes into being the old forms, naturally, continue to exist but they only play an insignificant part in further progress because they develop at a rate which is slower by several orders than that of the rate of development of the new form. We have seen this in the case of the origin of life, when the old abiogenic methods of synthesis of organic compounds were pushed into the background. This may also be expected to happen to the more rapid biological syntheses in connection with the transition from the biological to the social form of the movement of matter.

Human beings have hardly changed biologically for thousands of years, but during that time they have acquired an untold accession of power over the world around them and this power is the result of a common social development, not of an individual biological one.

The main highway of human progress does not now lie through the biological development of human individuals but through the improvement of their common life, through progress in the social form of the movement of matter.

BIBLIOGRAPHY

BERNAL, J. D.   *The physical basis of life.* London, Routledge, 1951.

BLUM, H. F.   *Time's arrow and evolution.* Princeton, N.J., Princeton University Press, 1955.

BRACHET, J.   *Biochemical cytology.* New York, Academic Press, 1957.

BUNGENBERG DE JONG, H. G.   *La coacervation, les coacervats et leur importance en biologie.* (*Actualités sci. industr, no.* 398). Paris, Hermann, 1936.

CALVIN, M.   *Science,* **130**, 1170 (1959).

DARWIN, F.   *Life and letters of Charles Darwin,* Vol. 3, p. 18 (footnote). London, Murray, 1887. (See also other works of Charles Darwin).

DIXON, M. and WEBB, E. C.   *Enzymes.* London, Longmans, 1958.

ENGELS, F.   *Dialectics of nature* (trans. C. Dutt). Moscow, Foreign Languages Publishing House, 1954.

FLORKIN, M.   *Biochemical evolution* (trans. S. Morgulis). New York, Academic Press, 1949.

FREY-WISSLING, A.   *Macromolecules in cell structure.* Cambridge, Mass., Harvard University Press, 1957.

GIESE, A. C.   *Cell physiology.* Philadelphia, Saunders, 1957.

KLUYVER, A: J. and VAN NIEL, C. B.   *The microbe's contribution to biology.* Cambridge, Mass., Harvard University Press, 1956.

KOSHTOYANTS, KH. S.   *Osnovy sravnitel'noĭ fiziologii.* Moscow, Izd. AN SSSR, 1957.

KREBS, H. A. and KORNBERG, H. L.   *Energy transformations in living matter.* Berlin, Springer, 1957

LEHNINGER, A. L.   *Revs. mod. Phys.* **31**, 136 (1959).

LENIN, V. I.   *Materializm i empiriokrititsizm.* (*Sochineniya,* Vol. 14). Moscow, Gospolitizdat, 1954.

LYSENKO, T. D.   *Agrobiologiya.* Moscow, Sel'khozgiz, 1948.

MILLER, S. L.   *J. Amer. chem. Soc.* **77**, 2351 (1955).

OPARIN, A. I.   *The origin of life on the Earth* (trans. A. Synge). Edinburgh, Oliver & Boyd, 1957.

OPARIN, A. I. et al. (ed.).   *Proceedings of the first international symposium on the origin of life on the Earth* (English-French-German edition). London, Pergamon, 1959.

PALADE, G. E. In *Microsomal particles and protein synthesis* (ed. R. B. Roberts) p. 36. London, Pergamon, 1958.

PAVLOV, I. P. *Sobranie sochinenii.* Moscow, Izd. AN SSSR, 1951-2.

PRIGOGINE, I. *Introduction to the thermodynamics of irreversible processes.* Springfield, Ill., Thomas, 1955.

SCHROEDINGER, E. *What is life?* Cambridge, University Press, 1945.

SECHENOV, I. M. *Izbrannye proizvedeniya.* Moscow, Uchpedgiz, 1958.

SCHMIDT, O. YU. *Chetyre lektsii o teorii proiskhozhdeniya Zemli.* Moscow, Izd. AN SSSR, 1950.

SISAKYAN, N. M. *Biokhimiya obmena veshchestv.* Moscow, Izd. AN SSSR, 1954.

UREY, H. C. *The planets, their origin and development.* New Haven, Conn., Yale University Press, 1952.

WIENER, N. *Cybernetics, or control and communication in the animal and the machine.* New York, Wiley, 1949.

WIENER, N. *The human use of human beings: cybernetics and society.* Boston, Mass., Houghton, Mifflin, 1950.